The Panama Canal

Also by Rolt Hammond:

FOUNDATION ENGINEERING

ENGINEERING STRUCTURAL FAILURES

POWER STATIONS WORK LIKE THIS

THE FORTH BRIDGE AND ITS BUILDERS

MOBILE AND MOVABLE CRANES

EARTHMOVING AND EXCAVATING PLANT

MODERN PILING PRACTICE

MODERN CIVIL ENGINEERING PRACTICE

DICTIONARY OF CIVIL ENGINEERING

WATER POWER ENGINEERING

TUNNEL ENGINEERING

GLOSSARY OF WELDING TERMS

RAILWAYS TOMORROW

AUTOMATIC WELDING

THE MAKING OF A SHIP

DIVING AND SALVAGE

HARBOURS AND DOCKYARDS

ROLT HAMMOND

and

WING COMMANDER C. J. LEWIN

The Panama Canal

FREDERICK MULLER

First published in Great Britain 1966 by
Frederick Muller Ltd,
Fleet Street, London, E.C.4
Printed by Ebenezer Baylis and Son, Limited
The Trinity Press, Worcester, and London
Bound by The Leighton-Straker Bookbinding Co. Ltd.

We are grateful to the United States Information Service, London, for supplying information and photographs, and also to Professor B. G. Maegraith, F.R.C.P. of the School of Tropical Medicine, Liverpool, and Dr. K. Neville Irvine, who have kindly checked the medical information in this book.

CONTENTS

PHOTOGRAPHS

FIGURES IN TEXT

1

RAILWAY PIONEERS

EVER since Hernando de la Serna explored the Chagres River and the Rio Grande in 1527, and opened up a route across the Isthmus of Panama, that great barrier has been a challenge to all who followed with schemes for building railways and canals.

It is interesting to reflect that for more than two centuries this route was the highway for Spanish treasure, transported by pack trains from the mines of Peru to the mother country. With the fall of the Spanish Empire it ceased to be an artery of world trade, but the idea of building a canal across the Isthmus owes its origin to French pioneering enterprise, and most of all to that remarkable man, Ferdinand de Lesseps.

In the long and chequered history of the Isthmus, there can be few more quixotic figures than William Paterson, a clever but erratic economist. Born in a Scottish farmhouse in 1658, he travelled to escape from religious persecution in his native land, and wandered as a pedlar through England. Later he went to the New World as a preacher and buccaneer by turns, a kind of Jekyll-and-Hyde existence, during which period he founded the astonishing project known as the Darien Scheme, a product of his fertile brain; another was the Bank of England. It is doubtful if he ever was a buccaneer, but it is believed that he gave much spiritual help to his companions under conditions that must often have imposed heavy strains upon them.

Returning to England from the Bahamas, this adventurer tried to interest James II in his Darien Scheme. It had the aim of establishing, through a powerful organization, a settlement on the Isthmus of Darien, which would according to Paterson "hold the key of the world's commerce". He elaborated this grandiose idea still further by explaining that ships of all nations were to be admitted to the projected harbour; that free trade with the whole world was to be maintained, and that differences of race and religion were to be annulled in the settlement. The Government refused to back the scheme, and it was also turned down by those of Berlin, Hamburg and Amsterdam.

Not to be discouraged, Paterson threw himself into commerce, resolved with Scottish perseverance to make a fortune so that he himself could carry out the scheme. As part of his enterprise, in 1690 he was concerned with the formation of the Hampstead Water Company. Four years later he produced a scheme for a bank, under which the subscribers would lend money to the nation, and the debt would form the bank stock. The Government required money, the plan was adopted, and so the Bank of England came into being, with Paterson as a director.

At this time the East India Company controlled the trade between England and the Orient, through a powerful monopoly. Paterson saw in this an opportunity to arouse the interest of his own countrymen in the Darien Scheme, which he took to Edinburgh, where he "soon had the whole Scottish people with him". Scotland had recently passed an Act for encouraging Foreign Trade, and in company with James Chiesly (an interloper whose name was used as a general term of abuse to cover unauthorized traders who tried to interfere with established trade monopolies), Paterson obtained a further Act of the Scottish Parliament for a Company franchise. This was to bear the title of an African and Indian Company, with a capital of £600,000, which was at once over-subscribed. However, owing to the jealous action of the East India Company, the London subscriptions were cancelled. The Darien Scheme was not at first included in this, but it formed the main issue when floated.

The ships set sail "amid the tears and prayers and praises of relations, friends and countrymen". Yet in spite of these heartfelt good wishes, the expedition was very badly managed, and even fraud entered into its activities, but not on the part of Paterson. A town called New Edinburgh was formed at Darien, but quarrels broke out amongst the members of the council in charge, originating mainly from the activities of the fanatical Kirk party. Fever attacked the colony and many people died, including Paterson's wife and children, but the promoters in Scotland continued their support, collecting further large sums of money to support other expeditions.

As was to be expected, Spaniards attacked the settlement, with the result that proclamations were issued against it by the home Government. Finally, complete disaster overtook the venture, the colonists being weakened by fever and hunger, with the result that the survivors capitulated to the Spaniards and marched to their ships with only the honours of war. Out of a total complement of two thousand who left the Clyde in hopes of fortune, only a few hundred survived. The Company failed, having lost £300,000 in this fantastic Scottish dream of universal free trade and a Darien colony.

The idea of cutting a canal was raised at an early date. In addition to proposed routes through Panama and Darien, two other possible routes were those of Nicaragua and Tehuantepec in Mexico, where later a railway was built by Lord Cowdray. In 1550 the Portuguese navigator, Antonio Galvao, published a book in which he explained that a canal could be built at any of these places; and in 1551 Gomara, the Spanish historian, recorded how he tried to persuade Philip II of Spain that such a project could be carried out.

However, this idea did not meet with the approval of the Spanish Government. In those days it was considered that a passage by sea to Cathay or China was regarded as of less importance than the monopoly of communications with the colonial possessions that Panama ensured, and the comparative security the barrier of the Isthmus then afforded. It was even forbidden under pain of death to seek or to make known any route between the oceans beyond that across the Isthmus to Panama. In those days the Church represented to Philip that "if the Almighty had intended there should be a waterway across the Isthmus one would have existed naturally". With the exception of the disastrous Paterson scheme in 1698, the project for a canal remained in abeyance. In 1771 other ideas were brought forward, and the Spanish Government caused a survey to be made of the Tehuantepec Isthmus. This route was found to be impracticable, however, and in 1779 surveys of the Nicaraguan route were made, but the project was dropped owing to political disturbances in Europe.

Horatio Nelson saw his first active service in an expedition he made in 1780 to San Juan de Nicaragua, where he nearly died of fever. This expedition had followed on a survey by a Spanish expedition on a route for a proposed Nicaraguan Canal. This project did not receive support from the Spanish Government, who had authorized the survey, but two British agents had accompanied the Spanish commission that made the report, and they sent a secret communication to the British Government, stating that the undertaking was possible.

When war was declared against England by Spain, the British Government decided to send an expedition, no doubt having been strongly influenced by the secret report, to Nicaragua, and Captain Nelson was appointed chief of the naval operations involved. In his despatch from Nicaragua, Nelson gave a favourable account of the possibilities of building an interoceanic waterway. Indeed, he went so far as to state his intention of occupying Lake Nicaragua, which he regarded as "the inland Gibraltar of Spanish America", commanding the water pass between the Atlantic and the Pacific, the possession of which would divide Spanish America into two parts. These British efforts were overcome, not by the Spaniards, who had been completely defeated by the British expedition, but by the forces of nature, represented by the rainy season and the fevers accompanying it. It is related that of the two-hundred-man crew of Nelson's ship, one hundred and ninety perished and were buried in Nicaragua, and Nelson's health was permanently injured.

Before reviewing what the French accomplished, and they did a great deal in the face of the most appalling difficulties, let us consider briefly the efforts of American railway promoters to construct a line across the Isthmus, headed by John Lloyd Stephens who, in 1847, collaborated with two financiers, Aspinwall and Chauncey, in promoting the Panama Railroad Company in New York. Stephens was a distinguished travel writer of his day, and resembled de Lesseps in that he was a diplomat; he was also a man of vision, who fully realized the vital importance of linking the two oceans by rail.

The United States Congress, in 1848, awarded contracts to two steamship lines to provide services to Panama, where the traffic would be linked by a river transit route. The contract for the line from New York to New Orleans and Chagres was awarded to George Law, and that from Panama to California and Oregon was taken by Aspinwall, who did not expect to make much from the shipping traffic alone, but had his sights set on wider issues. He imagined a great transport development, in which the railway crossing the Isthmus would link up the two shipping lines, and would stimulate trade throughout the whole Pacific basin; it would also have an effect on trade with China, Australia and the East Indies.

In those days, ships generally stopped at Chagres, near the old fort of San Lorenzo, where passengers transferred to dugouts and had to jump with their hand-luggage into small boats rising and falling in the swell alongside the ship. Often they had to land at Chagres in dangerous surf, and the boats, loaded with passengers, were poled slowly up the Chagres, stopping overnight at small villages. In the dry season they could reach Gorgona and in the wet season they got to Las Cruces. At these points the sorely tried passengers were transferred to mule trains for the journey to Panama City, and they had to face an exhausting journey of four or even eight days.

It was hardly surprising that considerable public interest was displayed in the proposed Panama Railroad, and in the winter of 1847–8 a preliminary survey was undertaken to determine the exact conditions of travelling. Stephens and his two partners, accompanied by James L. Baldwin, explored the suggested route, which would follow the valleys of the Chagres and the Obispo Rivers to the continental divide, where they discovered a 300-ft. pass, and then down the valley of the Rio Grande to Panama.

Having proved that their plan was practicable, they sought and obtained a concession from New Granada, which later became Colombia, and this concession was signed in Washington on December 28th, 1848. The terms were similar in many respects to those of the concession previously obtained by Mateo Klein for a French company, but this was forfeited in June, 1848. The scheme put forward by the American promoters was based on the idea of eliminating the long journey to the West via Cape Horn and also opening up a much shorter voyage to Asia, Australia and the Far East. The company was left free to decide whether the new route was to be entirely by rail, a combination of steamer and railway, or a macadamized road for horse traffic.

On April 7th, 1849, the company obtained a charter from the New York State Legislature to build and maintain the Panama Railroad. The capital was a mere 1,000,000 dollars, with the option that it could be raised to 5,000,000 dollars, a figure that was amended to 7,000,000 dollars in 1855. Early in 1849 a party of American engineers under Colonel George Hughes carried out location surveys, based on information collected from earlier surveys undertaken in 1827 and 1843, together with a vast amount of further valuable knowledge gained from the various trails through the nearby jungles.

This preliminary work was followed by a search for good engineers by Stephens and Aspinwall, and they were fortunate in discovering Colonel George Totten and John C. Trautwine, who made a world-wide reputation for himself with his famous civil engineer's pocket-book. These two men were the leading engineers of their day in the United States, and they had also carried out many important works in Colombia of the Del Dique Canal from Cartagena to the Magdalena River. Perhaps their most valuable qualification was their close familiarity with construction in the tropics, combined with their knowledge of handling labour under tropical conditions. They were appointed joint engineers of the new work.

Initially it was planned to start construction at Gorgona on the Chagres River, 30 miles from the Atlantic, in a central position that rapidly eliminated the dreadful pack-mule trip of 20 miles from Gorgona to Panama City. It was decided to continue construction towards the Atlantic at a later date. Trautwine set up his headquarters at Gorgona in January, 1850, from where he started the final survey towards Panama. Unfortunately, both he and his officers were laid low with fever, and the two river steamers built to ascend the Chagres to Gorgona were unable to do so in spite of their exceptionally small draft of 18 in. After a delay of some four months, it was decided to start railway construction at the Atlantic end of the line.

The discovery of gold in this part of the world in 1848 was a totally unexpected and dramatic development, and the news travelled round the world in a surprisingly short time despite the lack of rapid communication. A great flood of immigrants resulted, and prices rose and values were dislocated to such a degree that the railway contract which Totten and Trautwine had accepted suddenly became impossible. Eventually, a new contract for the job was signed on April 15th, 1850, with the Minister of Foreign Affairs in Bogotà, Don Victoriano de Diego Paredes, and it was approved by Colombian Congress on June 4th, 1850. Its provisions included a clause that the line should be completed in six years, with a monopoly of transport, including possible river and canal navigation with the provision of free ports at the terminals of the line.

After Colonel Totten had returned to the work, Trautwine and Stephens left for New York to discuss plans with the directors for the dry season and to recruit more labour. Colonel Totten and Baldwin continued clearance work and surveys, often working up to their waists in mud and water. At Monkey Hill, timber was dragged through swampland to use for the building of shanties on high ground. After two miles of location had been decided, railway construction was started in August, 1850, near Mount Hope Station. The line was laid southwards towards Gatun, where terminal facilities were started and a town laid out. In August the total labour force was four hundred, which by December had grown to a thousand; the turnover was large, however, and many left for more lucrative jobs elsewhere.

By April, 1851, most of the track from Manzanillo Island to Gatun had been laid. The original rails to Gatun were flat iron bars resting on timber stringers, which were replaced later by wrought iron rails of U section; these in turn were replaced by T section rails in 1869. A gauge of 5 ft. was adopted, for in those days rail gauges had not been standardized.

Work proceeded apace, docks were built at Limon Bay, so that ships could discharge materials for railway construction; they also brought in workers as passengers. However, after more than two years of work on construction since the granting of the charter, less than eight miles of line had been finished. The result was that the original 1,000,000 dollars were nearly expended, and the market price of the stock fell sharply. By September, 1851, the people in Panama City impatiently awaited news of the first train, expecting far more economic benefits to be obtained from the railway than were in fact achieved. On October 1st, 1851, a train of work cars travelled from the terminus at Gatun, and this was the first train on the new railway.

In November of that year, the *Georgia* and the *Philadelphia*, two American ships, arrived at the open roadstead off Chagres, but rough seas forced them to take refuge in Limon Bay, where the passengers were landed. This practically forced the railway to take passengers to Gatun, and established Limon Bay as the normal port of call which replaced Chagres. The confidence of investors in New York was restored, and financing of the line was resumed.

Railway construction was pushed ahead to Bohio Soldado, over a section of track that passed through what was known locally as Black Swamp, a 3,000-ft. length of silt and water, where Colonel Totten had been unable to find bottom at a depth of 180 ft. It was at this critical stage in its history that the Panama Railroad published its first timetable in the *Panama Herald*, announcing daily departures from Bohio Soldado to Aspinwall, for a fare of 2 dollars per passenger. At this time the line was 16 miles distant from Aspinwall, and 31 miles had still to be completed. The passengers, after leaving the train, still had to pole their way in native boats to Gorgona or Cruces before the final arduous journey on mule back to Panama.

A sandstone quarry was opened up at Bohio Soldado for the railway, and although this rock was soft, it was sound and could be quarried in large sizes. It was used for the construction of bridge piers and abutments, drains and other structures which, after a period of twenty years, was found to be in excellent condition. A further section of the line was opened in May, 1852, but the rainy season slowed down outside work. By the end of that month, however, trains were leaving Tavernilla and the company planned to carry on to Barbacoas, named after the Indian word for bridge, and there the railway would cross the Chagres. It was decided to complete the line from that point by contract with M. C. Story, who contracted to build the Barbacoas bridge and complete the line in one year.

By July, nearly 24 miles of the line had been built and 25 miles still remained to be constructed, but hardly had the train service been extended to Barbacoas when the line received its first test by the United States Army. On July 6th, 1852, eight companies of the Fourth Infantry, numbering about seven hundred, including families, together with some three hundred additional passengers, arrived at Aspinwall on board the steamer *Ohio*, on passage to California for garrison duty. They landed too late for the single train of the day, and the regiment had to stay the night in Aspinwall. By the following morning, most of their baggage had been loaded on to cars, but the locomotive proved to be too light for more than half the troops, so that two trains had to be despatched at an interval of one hour, the baggage being left for a later trip.

At Barbacoas, where rail facilities for transport to Panama City ended, the regiment was divided, the main body continuing to Gorgona by the slow and painful method of pole-propelled boats and then marching to Panama. One company under the regimental quartermaster Captain U. S. Grant (later President Grant) with the sick, women and children, as well as the baggage, was ordered to Cruces, a few miles beyond Gorgona. There mule transport to Panama was supposed to have been arranged, under the terms of a previous army contract by which the steamship company assumed cost and responsibility for transport of the regiment to California by land and sea. Unfortunately, however, the company's local agent could not obtain mules for the troops because of higher prices paid by civilian passengers. Grant waited three days, and then he himself hired mules at double the agent's price, charging it to the shipping company, and resumed his journey to Panama.

Owing to delay and exposure to rains at Cruces, combined with the difficulties experienced by the troops at Gorgona in making headway in the mud, transport was not carried out according to plan. Cholera and fever attacked the troops along both these routes, and the small guard at Cruces was so reduced in size that the baggage had to go unprotected. In fact, it was so permeated by local infection that some of it had to be destroyed. As if this were not enough, the troops consumed contaminated fruit and drank water at various points along the road, so that sickness greatly increased. Those troops who eventually arrived at Panama were wet, muddy and completely dispirited; some were drunk or sick and many died in the mud on the way.

Thus the regiment, after a delay of four weeks on the Isthmus, finally reached California late in August, by which time some eighty men had died, as well as nearly the same number of women and children. An interesting sidelight on this terrible business was later revealed during Grant's first term as President, when he secured from Colombia and from the United States Congress the authority that enabled the United States Navy to conduct the first comprehensive survey of Isthmian canal routes between 1870 and 1875.

The railway lost no time in pushing on with construction of the bridge spanning the Chagres at Barbacoas, where the river was 300 ft. wide and liable to great and sudden changes during heavy rains, becoming a destructive torrent. When the bridge was nearing completion, one span was swept away by a sudden freshet of the Chagres, and continuation of the line was held up during the dry season of 1852.

It was a great blow to the company when John L. Stephens died, for he had been the guiding genius of the whole enterprise. He had been exposed to both hardship and disease, as a result of which he returned to New York, where he died on October 13th, 1852. He was succeeded by William Young. Further work was held up by new difficulties, such as the collapse of the bridge and the deaths of workmen, a foretaste of what was to happen during the early days of constructing the Canal.

There was grave public dissatisfaction about the loss of passengers' luggage, and sometimes passengers were forced to wait in Panama for delivery of valuables, so that they lost their ships. The rate for a passenger from Cruces to Panama by mule was 18 dollars per person and 17 cents per pound for the luggage, high sums for those days.

Further reorganization of the company followed. The contractor, unable to handle the work within the price limit, was relieved of his contract and the work was taken over by the company who carried it out by direct labour. Young resigned and was succeeded by David Hoadley as President. More labour was recruited and men came from all over the world, and particularly from Ireland, India, China, England, France and Germany, more than seven thousand men in all. They were selected because they were physically fit, but the climate of Panama soon took its toll of them, and many left. The Company made strenuous efforts to meet their special needs, and even provided the thousand Chinese workmen with "hill-rice, their tea and opium". However, these men were so unhappy that many of them committed suicide, which gave rise to a legend that Matachin was named to commemorate these sad deaths, the Spanish word *mata* meaning kill, and *Chino*, Chinese. Yet it is of historical interest to point out that Matachin is marked on maps of this region published in 1678. Disease and desertions became so heavy that a large number of Jamaicans had to be taken on, and construction started once more.

The first job to be tackled was the rebuilding of the Barbacoas bridge spanning the Chagres, 625 ft. long and 18 ft. wide, constructed of wrought iron girders and standing 40 ft. above water level. The bridge was claimed at the time to be one of the "longest and finest iron bridges in the world". It was so strong that it lasted for more than half a century and was used even after the United States had occupied the Canal Zone. Along the rest of the line, many temporary bridges were replaced by permanent ones and culverts. The original sleepers of soft wood were replaced by sleepers of lignum vitae, a wood so hard that holes had to be drilled in it before spikes could be driven, and so durable that when sections of the line were taken up in 1910 the sleepers were still in good condition.

By June, 1853, the company had erected buildings for the use of workmen near Panama City, and it was rumoured that the company had bought the Flamenco, Perico and Naos Islands. Access to deep water at Panama City had for a long time been the chief aim of those engaged in shipping, as the large tidal range on the Pacific caused ships to ground at low tide in the harbours. Progress in other respects was so rapid that it was confidently expected that the whole line would be completed by August, 1854.

In November, 1853, Colonel Totten was able to forecast the problems facing him for completion of the line. In order to prepare for the approaching dry season, he reported conditions to the directors. More than seven miles of grading had been completed from the Chagres River to Obispo and some three miles of track had been laid over this section. It was expected that the Barbacoas bridge would be completed by December 1st, which would have enabled trains to run to Gorgona and the Obispo River by January 1st, 1854. The Cruces road had been repaired, and a branch road from it to the Obispo had been built. It was therefore planned to transfer passengers and freight from the steam train to pack-mules when the trains reached Obispo.

Grading and clearance had started along the right of way and at Panama. Of the 48 miles total length, some 23 miles were in operation at Barbacoas and it was expected that 30 miles would be in operation by January 1st, 1854, leaving only 18 miles to be completed. It was over this remaining section that the summit ridge had to be crossed at an elevation of 250 ft. above Pacific high water level. Colonel Totten considered that the ground was favourable, the largest cut at the summit amounting to 30,000 cub. yds., being 1,300 ft. long and 24 ft. deep. On the basis of performance by Mr. Story, he estimated that with 4,750 men at work the line could be completed to the Pacific within six months, or by August, 1854, but he hesitated to give an exact prediction. It was as well that he made this qualification, because predictions for later works were to be sadly out of line with the facts.

Great difficulties had still to be overcome. All materials, even sleepers, had to be imported, either from the United States or from Colombia. Workers also had to be imported, at a cost per worker that varied from 15 to 20 dollars. Story emphasized, however, that the effect of sickness had been grossly exaggerated and he revealed that it had in fact been less than the average for similar works undertaken in the United States. Enough iron was already on the Isthmus, and the remaining expenditure to complete the line was estimated at 1,426,800 dollars.

The company had at that stage eight locomotives, twelve first-class passenger cars, a hundred platform cars and a hundred wagons for excavated material; there was also a carpenter's and a blacksmith's shop and the entire line employed 1,400 men with main offices and repair shops at Aspinwall. The construction force had grown to 2,500 men, with 1,200 at work on the Obispo section. On November 24th, 1853, the opening of the Barbacoas bridge was celebrated in a suitable manner. Late in September, 1854, the line was completed to the summit, and of the remaining section to Panama City only four miles of grading and seven miles of rail laying remained to be completed. Construction gangs worked from both ends to hasten the day of completion, and on October 28th another landmark of progress was the publication of a timetable of trains from Aspinwall to the Summit.

At last, on January 27th, 1855, the great day arrived when the two advancing rail-laying gangs were in sight of each other, and at midnight, "in darkness and rain, the last rail was laid" at Summit, at a point 37 miles from Aspinwall and about 10 miles from Panama City. The next day crowds gathered along the line to see the train come "thundering over the summit, and down the Pacific slope" on what was described at the time as a "perilous journey, over fearful chasms, through mountain gorges, along pleasant valleys, winding around hoary mountain tops, perched upon a narrow shelf of rock in mid-air". As the train came into Panama City, the people were greatly impressed by its appearance and by the "facility with which the wild creature was handled", and they greeted it with hearty cheers. However, the local inhabitants soon realized that the railway was not the answer to their economic problems, for those who had been in the pack-mule business were thrown out of work, and business did not increase at once to offset this loss. Moreover, they were not consoled by the rates that the company charged: 25 dollars each way across the Isthmus, although special monthly season tickets costing 50 dollars were granted to residents.

The rates were exceptionally high for those days, and it was never explained why this policy was adopted, although the Superintendent of the line, Colonel Center, once stated that they "were intended to be, to a certain extent, prohibitory, until we could get things in shape". But the rates remained high for years and the line gained a reputation as a good dividend payer.

On Saturday morning, February 17th, 1855, directors and stockholders, steamship agents and guests embarked on the *Columbus* for a trip to Taboga Island. Landing amid the roar of guns from all the ships in the harbour, they were given lunch by Captain Wild of the British ship *Bolivia*, with the "substantiality and cordiality of a good old English welcome". This was followed by a visit to the steamer *John L. Stephens*, which had made the passage around the Horn. During the afternoon there was a heavy tropical shower, which drenched many of the guests but did not damp their enthusiasm for the celebrations. Eight guests were entertained to dinner in the evening by Colonel Totten at Aspinwall House. Toasts were drunk to the President of the United States, the Governor of Panama, the President of the Panama Railroad Company, the press and the agents of the shipping companies. It was not until the following Tuesday that the exhausted guests returned to Aspinwall to embark on a ship for New York.

The line, as completed in 1855, was about 47½ miles long. Starting at Aspinwall on Manzanillo Island, the line followed Limon Bay, crossed the Mindi River and reached the Chagres at Gatun. Then, following the valley of the Chagres, it crossed the river at Barbacoas by the new bridge and continued along the Chagres to the Obispo River, whose valley it followed on its way to Summit. After having passed over the summit, the line descended along the valley of the Rio Grande to Panama City. When the line had been completed in 1859 the total cost came to 8,000,000 dollars.

Deaths among the construction workers were not large. The Chinese, however, resisted medical treatment, exposed themselves to bad weather, smoked opium, and eventually, in a panic-stricken state, many of them committed suicide. Out of a total labour force estimated by Colonel Totten to have been about 6,000 there were 835 deaths, including 295 white men, 140 coloured men and 400 Chinese. During construction, about 140,000 sleepers were used in the track, so that the widely quoted saying that this work represented a "dead man for every tie" was quite wrong and completely misleading.

It is very important to realize that the railway had a decisive influence on the choice of route for the Panama Canal when it eventually came to be built. It provided much valuable information for the canal builders, and can be regarded as the pioneer venture in opening up communications across the Isthmus.

2

ENTER DE LESSEPS

DURING the time that the railway was being built, Ferdinand de Lesseps succeeded in opening up the Suez Canal to world shipping in 1869. He had built this great work in spite of almost incredible difficulties, and in spite of the fact that he was not an engineer but a diplomat. In fact, he disliked engineers, particularly when for sound technical reasons they held views and opinions that differed from his own. His success at Suez fired him with enthusiasm for a Panama Canal, and he now began to study the idea seriously.

The terrible disaster and defeat suffered by France in the Franco-Prussian War of 1870–71 served nevertheless as a spur to stimulate the French nation to offset it as much as possible by carrying out a great international work, and the general view in France was that the proposed Panama Canal would provide an ideal opportunity for achieving this end. The original idea for a Panama Canal was put forward in 1871 at the International Geographical Congress at Antwerp, as a result of much exploration undertaken in Colombia by Anthoine de Gogorza, who was born in the United States of French parents and had lived for some years in Colombia. It was not until 1875, however, when de Lesseps presided over a meeting of the Geographical Society in Paris, that the subject once more attracted world-wide attention. Having experienced the overwhelming success of his sea-level canal at Suez, which was paying handsome dividends to a large number of small shareholders in France, rather than to powerful financiers, he advocated the construction of a sea-level canal at Panama from the very outset. His obstinate obsession with this basic fallacy was to lead him into great difficulties and eventual disaster.

At this historic meeting of 1875 there was inadequate knowledge of the problem to enable detailed discussions to be held, but de Lesseps maintained that a sea-level canal would be the only type capable of meeting navigation needs, and that the failure of past planners to examine a possible sea-level canal route was a grave error. A resolution was passed at the meeting for an international congress to collect evidence and all relevant information and make recommendations for a canal. A Committee of Initiative, with de Lesseps at its head, was formed and made strenuous efforts to obtain international collaboration in carrying out surveys.

In the meantime, interest in the Panama Canal was revived in the United States, where efforts to secure canal rights had been interrupted by the Civil War, but were revived by President Johnson. A treaty was signed with Colombia in 1869 but was rejected by the Colombian Senate. The administration of President Grant followed, negotiations were resumed, and a treaty was signed on January 26th, 1870. This was amended to such an extent by the Colombian Senate, however, that it was totally unacceptable to the United States Government. Further negotiations were transferred in 1873 from Bogotá to Washington, where they again failed.

During President Grant's first term in office as President, much survey and exploration work was authorized by Congress over various proposed routes, which included Darien, Tehuantepec, Nicaragua and Panama. These surveys took place during the period from 1870 to 1875 and were exceptionally thorough; they were also far better than any which had previously been undertaken. In March, 1872, Congress authorized the President to appoint an Interoceanic Canal Commission to study and report on these surveys and other material which had been collected; the report of the Commission was made in 1876 and it recommended the Nicaraguan route. After this, further attempts to renew negotiations with Colombia failed and attention was naturally turned towards Nicaragua.

At this stage of development, the United States was faced

with economic difficulties arising from a drought and a trade depression, so much so that the Appropriations Act of 1876 cut out all financial provisions for U.S. legations in Bolivia, Colombia and Ecuador, in addition to many in Europe. President Grant, under protest, was forced to withdraw the ministers and close those legations for the rest of his term of office.

This setback for American interests was of great benefit to French promoters, and de Gogorza was able to work freely in Bogotá. He successfully convinced the Colombian Government that he had found a practicable route for a canal in the San Blas district where the Atrato and Tuyra Rivers could be used. On May 28th, 1876, he obtained a contract requiring that a report on explorations should be presented within a period of eighteen months. He returned to France.

Events were also moving rapidly in Paris, where the Geographical Society had organized the Committee of Initiative to examine the whole subject of a proposed interoceanic canal, with de Lesseps as President and Admiral Baron de la Roncière Noury, President of the Geographical Society, and J. L. Meurand, Director of Consulates in the Paris Foreign Office, as vice-president. Geographical knowledge of the Isthmus was very important, but it supplied only part of the immense amount of information required, so that it was necessary to provide finance for further surveys and exploration.

With this end in view, a limited company entitled La Société Civile Internationale du Canal Interocéanique was organized by General Istvan Türr, A.D.C. to the King of Italy; Lucien Wyse, a Lieutenant in the French Navy and grandson of Lucien Bonaparte; and the shrewd financier Baron Jacques de Reinach. The Society then took over the Colombian concession of de Gogorza. Wyse was a dominating figure, and was authorized to explore the Isthmus. He sailed for Panama with an assistant, but three of the eight engineers who went with him died on the way.

He divided his expedition into two groups and explored

several routes in the Darien and Atrato districts. Having completed his work in 1877, he returned to Paris in April of that year with plans which de Lesseps at once rejected because all required tunnels and locks. Wyse once more visited the Isthmus and started his second exploration on December 6th, 1877, this time in Panama. Here he examined two routes, that from San Blas and the other the present canal route from Limon Bay to Panama, choosing the latter. He planned a sea-level canal, conveniently close to the railway, but involving the construction of a tunnel 7,720 metres long through Culebra.

With his plan for a Panama Canal he left for Bogotá on horseback, a gruelling journey that took him eleven days. In Bogotá he negotiated what became the historic Wyse Concession and signed this with the Minister of Foreign Affairs, Don Eustorgio Salgar, on March 20th, 1878, the day that marks the legal start of the Panama Canal. He returned to France through New York, where he arranged for the control of the Panama Railroad. When he returned to France, he took with him his exploration reports, the Concession from Colombia, and the assurance of control of the railway which he required for help in the actual construction of the canal.

The International Congress for Consideration of an Interoceanic Canal (Congrès International d'Études du Canal Interocéanique) met in Paris on May 15th, 1879, under the temporary chairmanship of Admiral Roncière, with a total of 135 delegates, 74 from France, and eleven from the United States, some of whom were interested in Nicaragua and other canal areas. De Lesseps was elected President and Admiral Ammen vice-president. The Congress was organized in five committees. There was a Statistical Commission, its task being to determine the probable tonnage that would pass through the canal and to report on whether this would be sufficient to provide the expected return on the capital invested. It predicted that 5,250,000 tons would be the normal traffic, and that this would steadily increase after the assumed opening in 1889, and that 2,000,000 tons of cargo would be diverted from the trade then existing between Europe and Asia. The Secretary-General of the Suez Canal, on the basis of his experience, stated that it would be possible to handle a traffic of 6,000,000 tons per annum, on the assumption that fifty ships could pass through every day.

The Economic Commission reported on the distances that would be saved by its use, on the new markets and the new traffic that would be created, in addition to the reduction on freight and insurance that would result from the much shorter voyages and the avoidance of such danger areas as Cape Horn. This Commission also reported on the adverse effect of locks and tunnels on the handling of large ships.

The Commission of Navigation was composed of marine experts, with Dr. O. J. Broch, a Norwegian, presiding. It studied winds and currents as well as the effect of the proposed canal on shipbuilding, commenting that a lock canal would be acceptable only if it were proved to be impossible to build a sea-level canal. If a lock canal were adopted, however, it was considered that traffic would require "double locks, side by side, one for vessels going west and the other for vessels going east".

Perhaps the most important committee was the Technical Commission, on which served the most eminent engineers of that time, including Alexandre Lavalley and Abel Couvreux, who had been responsible for all the dredging work on the Suez Canal.

Many ideas were put forward for consideration by the Technical Commission, the members of which studied two particular routes, a sea-level plan at Panama and a plan for a canal with locks through Nicaragua. At its last meeting, on May 28th, 1879, the proposal for a sea-level canal from Colon to Panama was adopted, but the voting was by no means unanimous; there were several abstentions and contrary votes. Although all the Commissions were in favour of a sea-level canal, there were sharp differences of opinion, particularly amongst the engineers. One of these, Adolphe Godin de Lépinay, was strongly in favour of a lock canal, and his opinion was regarded with considerable respect since he was the only one who had actually supervised work on the Isthmus. He was familiar with the topography, knew what could happen if the torrential Chagres were not controlled, understood the problems of tropical labour and had seen the terrible effects of tropical diseases.

It was de Lépinay who pointed out that it would be necessary to cross a highland barrier at Culebra, and that the excavation of this huge mass of rock and soil would be an immense task, rendered even more difficult in a country ravaged by yellow fever. His plan for a canal was both simpler and cheaper. He drew attention to the fact that the headwaters of the two important Isthmian rivers approached each other near Culebra. The Rio Grande drained in a southerly direction into the Pacific, and the Obispo in a northerly direction into the Chagres and then into the Atlantic. The valleys of these two rivers were flanked by mountains and hills that provided natural areas for the formation of lakes. He thought this was the key to the problem.

His plan was remarkably simple. He proposed to create a large lake on each side of the continental divide by building a dam across the Chagres River and another one across the Rio Grande, as close to the sea as the topography permitted. The water in each artificial lake so formed would rise to the approximate level of 80 ft., and the two lakes would be linked together by a channel across the divide. Locks would then be built on each side of the Isthmus between the lakes and the sea level.

Yet his plan was rejected by the members of the Congress, who failed to appreciate its obvious merits. In fact they were too ignorant to be able to understand them, and these proposals were not even discussed seriously. This failure proved to be disastrous for the French project, as we shall see later.

When it came to a vote, de Lépinay was much disturbed and protested strongly against it, for he did not want to have his name linked with a scheme he regarded as being hopeless. Later events fully justified his opinions, and his confidence was not shaken, because he stated, "If I have not known how to make my advice triumph, I cannot let it be believed that I abandon it, all unknown though I am." He went on to point out that a lock canal would cost 500,000,000 francs less than a sea-level canal, that it would provide a more rapid transit, and that it would avoid the sacrifice of many lives. He added, "In order not to burden my conscience with these useless deaths and with the loss of a large capital, I abstain from voting, or I vote *No*."

With the benefit of hindsight that we have today, it is very difficult to understand why this simple plan should have been completely ignored. Had it been adopted, it would have eliminated nearly all excavation in the valleys of the Chagres and Rio Grande for the French Canal, except in the sea-level sections. Furthermore, it would also have greatly reduced the quantity of excavation in the Obispo Valley and in the Culebra Cut. Broadly speaking, it was the canal plan finally adopted by the United States in 1906.

In spite of all this, there was an enthusiastic meeting of the Congress in full session on May 29th, 1879, at which a resolution was passed for a "one-level" canal from Limon Bay to the Bay of Panama. The voting, however, was significant; of the 135 members 37 were absent, and of the remaining 98 the voting was 78 ayes, 8 nays and 12 abstentions. Admiral Ammen refused to vote, on the ground that only engineers should do so. Of the members 74 were French and 11 American; only 42 were engineers. Of the 78 who voted in favour 20 were engineers, but only one had visited Panama. Of the 11 United States delegates 4 were absent, 4 did not vote and 3 voted for Panama.

By this very unsatisfactory voting, then, the Congress approved a sea-level canal on a location from Limon Bay to Panama, at a cost of 214,000,000 dollars, allowing twelve years for completion, yet it would appear that most of the engineers were sceptical about the sea-level proposal. Charles

Kleitz, one of them, supported his contrary vote with the observation that the resolution was "too positive and too absolute". He agreed that the canal should run from Limon Bay to Panama, but considered that the surveys were not detailed enough to make a choice of type "based upon reasons and proofs".

De Lesseps persuaded the meeting to adopt his ideas, but he had foolishly ignored the advice of a well-qualified engineer and paid dearly for it. He praised the members of the Congress highly for the work they had done, and yielded the chair to Admiral Roncière, who made a glowing speech, ending it with the hope that "the illustrious gentleman who had been the soul of the deliberations, who was the personification of grand enterprises and who had charmed all by his courtesy and dignity, might live to witness the completion of the great work to which his name would remain forever attached, and of which he could refuse to take the direction". Not for nothing had de Lesseps been nicknamed the "Great Frenchman" and he replied to the Admiral's eulogy by saying, among other things, that "a general who has once gained a battle never refused to engage in another".

At this point it is appropriate that we should deal briefly with the career of this great man. He was born at Versailles on November 19th, 1805, into a family of traditional diplomats, he and his brothers receiving their primary education wherever their father happened to be diplomatically appointed. He completed his education at the Lycée Henri IV in Paris and then entered the Ministry of Foreign Affairs, whence he was appointed to the French Consulate General in Lisbon at the age of 20, returning to the Ministry two years later. He was later appointed Vice-Consul at Tangier, Cairo, Alexandria and to Consular posts at Malaga and Barcelona. For ten months he was French Ambassador in Madrid, and was then recalled to Paris to undertake a special mission to Rome.

His promotion in the French Foreign Service was very rapid, and is said to have aroused jealousy amongst his colleagues. In 1849 he resigned from the French Diplomatic Service at the early age of 44. He was undoubtedly a loyal and successful diplomat, but he never studied engineering, neither did he qualify as an engineer. Indeed, one of his most loyal colleagues in later years lamented his defects, saying that he was "blindly over-optimistic, obstinate and technically incompetent". Had this great man with so many outstanding qualities also been an engineer it is certain that the history of the Panama Canal would have been very different.

The people in Panama were overjoyed when they heard the news of the resolution which had been passed in Paris, and the optimistic statement by de Lesseps that he would raise 100,000,000 dollars in thirty days and thus be able to start the work. The reaction to this news in the United States was quite different, certain newspapers assuming a threatening tone and referring ominously to the Monroe Doctrine. This attitude was reflected in Congress by the introduction on June 25th, 1879, of a joint resolution by General Burnside that "the people of these States would not view without serious disquietude any attempt by the powers of Europe to establish under their protection and domination a ship-canal across the Isthmus of Darien" and that it would be regarded "as a manifestation of an unfriendly disposition toward the United States".

The French people were elated at the idea of building another great canal, for many of them still held to the doctrine of the religious fanatic Saint-Simon, who wrote of "social regeneration through work, and universal peace through great public undertakings, and particularly by developing communications between the peoples of the world".

This was all very well, but how was such a huge project as the Panama Canal to be financed? De Lesseps decided that the subscription method used with such success for the Suez Canal should also be employed for the new ocean artery. It should here be pointed out that at this stage in the scheme

2

de Lesseps was no longer young, having passed his seventy-third birthday. His family and friends tried to dissuade him from this gigantic undertaking, but he would not listen to their advice. He certainly did not need money at that time, for the Suez Canal was giving good results; he wanted the glory of a second victory. He paid no heed to the plea of his son Charles, who asked, ". . . for us who have worked at your side, are we to have no repose?" De Lesseps was convinced that the new canal could be completed in eight years at a cost of about 50,000,000 dollars, and claimed with some truth that the difficulties were "not so formidable as those which had to be overcome in the construction of the Suez Canal, as a railway already exists along the course . . . with a large town at each extremity".

The Universal Interoceanic Panama Canal Company (Compagnie Universelle du Canal Interocéanique de Panama), to be known later as the Old Panama Company, was formed with a capital of 400,000,000 francs, in the form of 800,000 shares of 500 francs each. It was announced that de Lesseps would dig the first spadeful of earth on January 1st, 1880. De Lesseps himself proposed that General Grant should be the first honorary president of the Company, while he would serve as the general manager, but there was considerable opposition to this idea in the United States, and de Lesseps was made President.

In order to start the Company, four hundred founders' shares of 5,000 francs each were sold to those persons who were "interested in the creation of great enterprises", and to each of these a hundred additional free shares were given. By this means 2,000,000 francs were obtained. De Lesseps then acquired the Wyse Concession from the society headed by General Türr for the high price of 10,000,000 francs. A public subscription was organized for August 6th and 7th, and circulars were sent out to the United States and Europe announcing the formation of the Company, with an expected annual income of 90,000,000 francs and dividends to be paid at the rate of 11·5 per cent, an optimistic forecast.

The opening of the campaign was marred by strong political attacks on the whole scheme; opponents maintained that the cost estimates were too small and the estimated receipts too great. Even in France the press and financial experts were hostile. In the United States the proposals aroused fears, which were increased by a rival campaign started by Admiral Ammen, and Menocal, a distinguished American civil engineer, for a canal through Nicaragua. De Lesseps was portrayed as a Bonapartist seeking power.

The result of this first campaign for support was a complete failure, only a mere 30,000,000 francs being subscribed, but de Lesseps was not deterred. He demanded new surveys and the sending to Panama of an International Technical Commission of eminent engineers, which he would accompany, and which would confirm that the Panama location was the most practicable route. Armed with this new knowledge, he would then travel to the United States and try to persuade Americans to back the canal. In order to help in overcoming opposition, he started a fortnightly bulletin on September 1st, 1879, entitled *Bulletin du Canal Interocéanique*, which was published until February, 1889. This probably inspired the *Canal Record*, a paper that the Americans later published.

Many eminent people took a keen interest in the project during the initial stage of promotion, and several spoke at the historic Paris Congress in May. Colonel Totten, now an old man, speaking from his experience of having constructed the Panama Railroad, had studied the canal problem and had submitted a scheme in 1857 for a lock canal from Limon Bay to Panama Bay. He laid down a bottom width of 150 ft. and a depth of 31 ft. Each lock was to be 400 ft. long and 30 ft. wide, and the summit level of 150 ft. to be supplied from a 24-mile feeder channel from the upper Chagres. The estimated cost of this proposal was 80,000,000 dollars.

Writing in October, 1879, after the Paris Congress, he pointed out that up to the end of the Congress the type of canal considered was still doubtful; that is, whether it should be a sea-level or lock canal, or a tunnel. But it had been decided that Panama was the best route. Although Colonel Totten considered that a sea-level canal was economically impracticable at that stage, he did say that "with enough money, science and perseverance" it could have been built.

The sea-level plan put forward by Wyse and Reclus allowed for a dam to be built in the Chagres River to control the floods. Colonel Totten considered that this was too dangerous, however, and his opinion was valuable since he had close experience of the country. He estimated that the cost of a sea-level canal, based on a bottom width of 105 ft. in earth and 120 ft. in rock, would be 344,000,000 dollars without a tunnel, and he added a further 85,000,000 dollars as the cost of diverting the Chagres River to Las Minas Bay, bringing the total sum to 429,000,000 dollars. This immense cost convinced him that a sea-level canal was impracticable.

The approaching visit to Panama of the Technical Commission was going forward, and de Lesseps undertook a lecture tour in France. Opposition to the canal continued to grow in the United States, yet American citizens resident in Panama were in favour of the idea. During the autumn of 1879 a party of engineers from France arrived at Panama with drilling equipment and began a series of borings supplemented by surveys in anticipation of visits by the consulting engineers.

On the afternoon of December 30th, 1879, de Lesseps arrived at Colon, and the city was decorated with the flags of all nations except those of the United States! A band played lively airs as he and his wife and three young children came ashore from the *Lafayette*, flagship of the French West Indies Squadron. In addition, there were eminent engineers of the International Technical Commission, who had come with him from France, and a group from the United States, which included T. W. Park, President of the Panama Railroad, as well as Colonel Totten, who had collaborated closely with the French engineers in their scheme.

At this stage, de Lesseps recognized two great difficulties:

control of the Chagres River, and the excavation of the gigantic cutting at Culebra, through the summit. He pointed out that the first problem would be solved by diverting the headwaters of the river "into another channel, and the second will disappear before the wells which will be sunk and charged with explosives of sufficient force to remove vast quantities at each discharge". His visit to Colon completed, de Lesseps left for Panama City by train, and all along the line there were scenes of enthusiasm for the Great Frenchman. At the Barbacoas bridge the President of the State of Panama boarded the train, and both he and de Lesseps were entertained to dinner on the way to Panama City, where elaborate preparations had been made for suitable festivities.

When the train reached its destination, the party proceeded to an open tent, where de Lesseps was introduced to the local dignitaries. From there they went in carriages to the Grand Hotel, along the Avenida Central, between lines of Colombian troops. The Avenida and the streets adjacent to it were decorated, the flags of France and Colombia predominating. At intervals there were shields, each bearing the name of earlier explorers, from Balboa in 1513 to Wyse, Reclus and Sosa in 1877 and 1878. Triumphal arches were also erected, that at the Plaza Santa Ana reading, "Colombia salutes Ferdinand de Lesseps", and the one at the Grand Hotel proclaiming, "Panama salutes her illustrious guest, Ferdinand de Lesseps".

All this junketing showed a complete lack of reality, which was fully borne out by the subsequent tragic happenings. Having inaugurated the canal at the mouth of the Rio Grande, de Lesseps decided to carry out a similar ceremony at the Culebra Cut on January 10th, 1880, and he went to Cerro Culebra, later known as Gold Hill, for the ceremony. An explosive charge, fitted with an electric detonator, had been laid in the hard basalt formation a few feet below the summit, and all was ready. There were many celebrities present, including Bishop Paul and de Lesseps' little daughter Ferdinande, to whom was given the honour of pressing the button to fire the charge. A large mass of rock was hurled into the air and the party returned to Panama full of enthusiasm and prophesying "perfect success".

The arrival of the French engineers and canal promoters had the effect of raising prices on the Isthmus and merchants were carried away with a "mania of sudden riches". Rent soared from 40 to 80 dollars a month and plots of land which had formerly been priced at 1,000 dollars were easily sold for 4,000. In order to counter this trend, the Company ordered prefabricated houses from Chicago, with the aim of establishing its own towns. The report of the International Commission was ready on February 14th, and contained replies to all the questions raised by de Lesseps. The line of the canal that the Paris Congress recommended was verified, only slight changes being made to reduce curvature. Trial borings to depths of 12 to 21 metres had been taken along the line of the canal and at the site of the Gamboa Dam. In order to ensure that the banks of the canal would be stable on each side, the Commission adopted a slope of forty-five degrees for all excavations, except along the summit section in Culebra Cut, where a slope of $\frac{1}{4}$ to 1 was recommended.

Generally speaking, the canal was to be a trench 72 ft. wide at the bottom and $27\frac{1}{2}$ ft. deep, on a route following the Panama Railroad. Starting at Colon, the canal would pass through six miles of lowlands to the Chagres Valley at Gatun. It would then follow the valley for about 21 miles to Gamboa, where it would curve right and follow the valley of the Obispo, crossing the continental divide at Culebra, and joining the Pacific Ocean by following the valley of the Rio Grande.

The success of the plan depended upon suitable measures being taken to control the Chagres River, for otherwise there would have been a huge waterfall from the higher bed of the Chagres into the canal at Gamboa. It was therefore proposed to build a dam 40 metres high to retain the waters of this river in a large lake. A new channel, the east diversion, would carry its waters to the Atlantic. For drainage on the opposite side, it was proposed to make a west diversion. South of the cordillera, an east and a west diversion would have to be constructed, thus making a total of five canals: one main canal and four diversion channels.

It was considered that no works would be necessary for terminal facilities, except for a tidal lock at the Pacific end of the canal where there was a considerable tidal range, as well as a breakwater at Colon where the anchorage was liable to be affected by northerly winds. The grand total excavation was estimated at 75,000,000 cub. metres and the estimated cost at 843,000,000 francs, a very much higher figure than that approved by the Paris Congress, which did not cover items for interest on capital and other expenses, totalling 409,000,000 francs. The report, signed by each member of the Technical Commission, with Colonel Totten's name at the head of the list, was later described by J. B. Bishop as both thorough and scientific.

During his visit, de Lesseps had obviously created an excellent impression on the local inhabitants. A fine horseman, he rode over the trails during his many inspections. He had many friends and attended church services and local functions. Even at his advanced age, he worked all day and enjoyed dancing at night, and on one occasion he crossed the Isthmus with Colonel Totten to attend a ball given in honour of him and his wife. Whilst at Colon, he selected a site for a statue of Columbus, which had been presented to Colombia by the Empress Eugénie of France.

On the way back to Paris, and during the voyage to New York, de Lesseps studied the engineers' report and revised the estimates of construction costs downward from 843,000,000 francs to 656,000,000 francs. It is very hard to understand how he was able to justify this departure from the estimates of experts, as he must have been only too well aware from personal inspection of the enormous difficulties that lay ahead. Perhaps he intended to try and convince the Americans to support the scheme on the basis of this lower estimate. We shall never know.

His arrival in the United States was greeted with a certain amount of hostility, although with considerable interest. A committee met him at the steamer and escorted him to his hotel for all too brief a rest. On March 1st, 1880, he opened his campaign with an address to the American Society of Civil Engineers. As he began to explain his scheme for a canal, his map suddenly fell to the floor. With ready wit he exclaimed, "Oh, there's my canal gone to the ground!" The map was at once picked up and replaced, and de Lesseps, adding with typical French gallantry, "But America has restored it to me", continued his address unperturbed. It should be pointed out that he was careful to explain he was a diplomat and not an engineer.

As regards the original capital of the Company, he made it quite clear that one-half of it could be raised in the United States. He took the opportunity once again of emphasizing his preference for a sea-level canal, and someone asked why a lock canal should not be built instead of a sea-level one, as recommended by the Technical Commission. He replied, "If the Committee had decided to build a lock canal I would have put on my hat and gone home." The audience was convinced, and de Lesseps ended the meeting with more friends in his favour.

The same evening he was entertained with typical American hospitality at Delmonicos, at that time the most famous New York restaurant. The room was decorated with flowers and flags, making an ideal setting for the coats of arms of the United States and France, as well as with scale models of the Suez and Panama Canals. There were 253 carefully selected guests and their ladies, representing financial, diplomatic, religious and political fields in the United States.

An eloquent speech of welcome was given by the Reverend Richard Storrs, who gave a word picture of the importance of communication in the interests of peace, recalling how de Lesseps had planned both the Suez Canal and the Corinth Canal as well as a railway from Europe to India. He also referred to the German geographer, Johannes Schoener, the namer of America, who made a globe in 1520 clearly showing the Isthmus of Panama, with a line drawn across it to represent a future Strait of Panama.

There were several other speeches during that long evening, and it was reported that the guests were impressed by the "magnificent freshness, enterprise and youth" of the man who sat there "crowned with the triumph of a desperate but successful victory" in overcoming deserts of Africa and joining the waters of the Mediterranean with those of the Red Sea. They wanted to see the same ability and experience applied to Panama.

In Washington, de Lesseps called on President Hayes. Although the interview appeared to have been successful, soon afterwards the President sent a message to the Senate on March 8th, 1880, calling for a "canal under American control" and declaring at the same time that the United States could not consent to "the surrender of this control to any European power or to any combination of European powers". The Government of the United States still remembered that ill-fated dream of a Mexican Empire that France had tried to create only twenty years previously in the tragic episode of Maximilian.

De Lesseps then toured the United States on a lecture tour, visiting San Francisco, Boston, Chicago and other cities. In Chicago he met with opposition, which infuriated him. During an address to a large audience at the Exchange, a questioner brought up the Monroe Doctrine. De Lesseps boldly answered, "Here are 20,000 of you Americans. Now explain to me how the Monroe Doctrine prevents my making the canal?" There was silence, followed by an explanation from de Lesseps that it would not operate against a canal. He added, "I cannot agree with a town only one-third my own age, though with 400,000 inhabitants, which says that the thing is impossible." "Hurrah! That's the boy we want!" shouted a member of the audience, and de Lesseps had gained another victory.

2*

Returning to New York after this exhausting trip, he rested for a very short time. The following morning there was a reception and luncheon at the home of Cyrus W. Field, one of the leading pioneers of the transatlantic cable. In the afternoon de Lesseps was again interviewed by the press, when he announced that shares to the value of 300,000,000 francs (600,000 shares of 500 francs each) would be offered for sale in the United States as soon as the necessary arrangements could be made in Paris for the formation of a banking syndicate in the United States. De Lesseps said that if the above amount of shares was bought in the United States she would "have a controlling voice in the enterprise". However, if no shares at all were sold, he said that he would still build the canal, being confident of success because he had a market for his securities in Europe. He went on: "In France and England I am confident that I can place all the shares if America does not wish to take any; but from my reception here I am of the opinion that the United States will be inclined to take a large proportion of them. At any rate I shall proceed with my canal."

The next day, April 2nd, 1880, the de Lesseps family were escorted aboard the White Star liner *Adriatic* by Cyrus W. Field, and sailed for France via England, Belgium and Holland. Although de Lesseps had been unable to sell his securities in the United States, where he had received widespread admiration, he did make many valuable American friends. On arrival at Liverpool, he offered shares to the value of £166,000 to the British public. In doing so, he stated that he would be able to complete the work in six years with a labour force of 8,000 men, a very rash statement considering the magnitude of the work involved.

He must have been a fascinating speaker, however, because he generally succeeded in taking his hearers along with him. Whilst in Brussels he announced that the work of building the canal would be undertaken by Messrs. Couvreux and Hersent, the same firm which had achieved such success at Suez. Bunau-Varilla suggested that this particular talk gave an interesting insight into the many errors to which de Lesseps obstinately clung, one of the reasons probably being that he disliked engineers. Bunau-Varilla went on, "he did not realize that, with new elements of labour, new sanitary conditions, excess of rainfall, and ground to excavate the nature of which was unknown" serious error could result from the advice of men whose "limited education deprives them of that suppleness of mind needed to foresee and to measure the unknown quantities in a new problem". The basic reasons for the disastrous French failure at Panama could not have been more suitably expressed.

After de Lesseps had spoken, he was followed by Abel Couvreux, who claimed that his firm would be prepared to build the canal at an estimated cost of 512,000,000 francs, a figure that still further reduced the previous inadequate estimates, but which he explained was possible in view of recent improvements made in the design and construction of excavating machinery. His firm wanted eight years to complete the contract: two for organization surveys and the assembly of materials, and six for the main work on the line of the canal. It is significant that twenty years later—in spite of immense improvements in excavating machinery—it required three years of preparatory work and seven years of intensive construction work for the United States to complete the work.

During that summer de Lesseps toured the cities of France, speaking in support of the approaching subscription, informing the public that the scheme had been investigated by the International Technical Commission, which had investigated the canal line on the Isthmus and declared that it was practicable. He also made it known that the contractors would be Couvreux and Hersent. The annual traffic had been estimated at 6,000,000 tons, which would produce a revenue of 90,000,000 francs. Later it turned out that at least his forecast of tonnage was justified.

Late in the summer of 1880 he was able to announce that financial obstacles to the canal were being resolved in the

United States, and that three bankers were to form a committee in New York. Furthermore, Richard W. Thompson resigned his Cabinet post as Secretary of the Navy to accept a position at the head of this committee at the attractive salary of 25,000 dollars a year and to become the promoter of the Panama Canal Company. Even so, it appeared at the time that American support for the scheme was being unduly delayed, but at last came the announcement that Panama stock would be offered for sale in December, 1880.

The selling movement gathered momentum, and practically every country in Europe took part, offices having been opened in Germany, Austria, Italy and England. In the *Bulletin du Canal* of November 15th it was announced that subscription would take place on December 6th, 7th and 8th, 1880. The capital structure was defined as 600,000 shares at 500 francs each, totalling 300,000,000 francs, with 590,000 shares available for the public and only 10,000 shares reserved for founders, the result of de Lesseps' desire to encourage the small investor. Shareholders in the Suez Canal Company were to have preference, with one share of Panama stock allowed for each share of Suez Canal stock. The subscription was announced as covering only half the cost of the canal, the total cost being estimated at 600,000,000 francs.

Another interesting point was that the *Bulletin* of the above date quoted a letter from de Lesseps answering his critics, whom he placed in two classes: those who presented false estimates to prove that the canal would not pay, and those who wished to inspire fear of the United States. To the first category he replied that the work would be done by the contractors who built the Suez Canal, and to the second he simply referred to his successful tour in the United States.

At this stage of promotion, the lack of financial interest revealed in the United States was more than counterbalanced by the remarkable enthusiasm and support shown in France. When the subscriptions were closed on December 9th, the public had subscribed 600,000,000 francs, more than twice the offering. Small investors were attracted because of the undoubted success of the Suez shares. In order to provide financial services, a Panama Bank was founded in Paris; a Commercial Panama Company was organized to supply food on site; and a general meeting of stockholders was held on January 31st. This was followed by a second meeting on March 3rd, when de Lesseps read his report, in which he stated that there were now 102,230 shareholders and the canal would be completed in 1888. The total volume of excavation was estimated at between 73,000,000 and 75,000,000 cub. metres, and the total cost of construction at 512,000,000 francs. Marine dredgers were to work at Colon and La Boca on the sea-level canal. In the very difficult and gigantic Culebra Cut, work would start in October, 1881. Between 8,000 and 10,000 men would be recruited from Colombia and the West Indies to work on the construction.

This outline was all too simple, and there were many misgivings, for those who knew the country also knew that de Lesseps was completely unfamiliar with it. He had not even lived there for a complete year, and was blind to the fact that the lessons learnt at Suez were simply not applicable to Panama, where conditions were completely different. Moreover, circumstances were such that he remained at home to raise money for a scheme that was so far away he could neither watch its progress nor correct mistakes when they arose. He grossly underestimated the cost through lack of technical knowledge, the company was always hard pressed for funds, and in addition he was getting too old for such an immense task.

He even tried to prove that the climate of Panama was no worse than it was anywhere in the Desert of Suez, and was completely ignorant of the terrible scourge of tropical diseases. The Government of Colombia, which appeared on the surface to be friendly, was so weak that it gave him practically no support, and was the cause of much delay and confusion. The resources of the whole region of Panama were so inadequate that practically every necessity for the work had to be imported. It was pointed out in the London

Standard of December 8th, 1880, that "in Panama de Lesseps has no gangs of Fellaheen forced to work for scant wages, no enthusiastic Khedive willing to command the resources of the State for the benefit of the undertaking".

3

THE FRENCH TRAGEDY

ON January 29th, 1881, the first French construction group arrived at Colon on board the *Lafayette* with a party of forty engineers and officials under the leadership of Armand Reclus, Agent-General of the Panama Canal Company. Five of these officials brought their wives to a land that had been falsely described in France as the "healthiest region in the world". Although luxuriant in vegetation, it was also a country in which the humidity was oppressive, life was monotonous and insects and diseases flourished. All this had been amply proved during the construction of the railway. The country, according to Lieutenant Charles Rogers, who crossed the Isthmus in 1881 before excavation started, was a mass of "thickly matted jungle", which could be penetrated only with the machete, a kind of billhook. Even today the jungle beyond the Canal Zone is just as thick as it ever was.

This party was probably the first actual construction organization of the Panama Canal. It consisted of a Superior Agency, a Real Estate Department, a Sanitary Service, and a Works and Construction Division. Its first task was to mark the exact location of the canal line, clear the timber and jungle along the line, and then open up the country for the heavy labour of excavation. This preparatory work was expected to take about a year, using a system of direct labour that was continued until Jules Dingler took charge in 1883.

The contract for the construction was signed with Couvreux and Hersent on March 12th, 1881, and they agreed to complete the work for 512,000,000 francs, but the contract was conditional in the sense that it was not to become binding until two years had elapsed. A director of the firm, Gaston Blanchet, went to the site to prepare preliminary plans, but found that there was much disagreement amongst the high officials, so he departed for Paris on April 5th to settle the "definite order and course" of the canal works which then began to take shape. A large frame-house was erected near Gatun, a sawmill was built at Colon, twenty small houses shipped from New Orleans were erected, and twenty more from France and fifty from New Orleans were ordered. In October deliveries of excavators and other machinery started from Europe.

A real obstacle to further progress at this stage was the modification of the concession granted to the Panama Railroad Company by the Government of Colombia, forcing de Lesseps to buy a controlling interest in the railway's capital stock by purchasing 70,000 shares of 100 dollars par value. It was not until August, 1881, that the French gained this control, and at a fantastic price. They paid 17,133,500 dollars for 68,534 shares at a price of 250 dollars per share, with a further 7,000,000 dollars for the company's bonds, and a bonus of 1,102,000 dollars to the directors. The grand total was 25,000,000 dollars, about one-third of the Canal Company's resources, and it was described by André Siegfried as "a real Stock Exchange holdup". However, this did at least give the French the necessary control of the Panama Railroad Company, which still retained its former status as a corporation established in New York, and was probably helpful where American public feeling was concerned.

All this time de Lesseps was keeping up a vigorous publicity campaign for his beloved Panama Canal, simultaneously running the affairs of the successful Suez Canal Company. But his enthusiasm and optimism seem to have run away with him, for he declared on one occasion that the Panama Canal would be completed in six years, and at another time in only four, in spite of the fact that the contract period had been planned as eight years. The Panamanian press was critical of this degree of optimism in Paris; it agitated for larger salaries and for more power to be granted to local officials. De Lesseps was able to use the Suez Canal success as a kind of bait to possible investors in the Panama scheme, declaring that the traffic through the Suez Canal had increased during the past year by 40 per cent, and that the remarkable profit of 12,979,000 francs, or 21 per cent, had been achieved, and also that he was preparing to light the Suez Canal with electricity in order to permit night transits.

The working force at Panama increased every month, but there was increasing illness among those who were not yet acclimatized. The first death from yellow fever among the 1,039 employees occurred in June, 1881, but later on the deaths from malaria exceeded those from yellow fever. By the autumn, materials had arrived by sea in such volume that the warehouses in Colon were filled, and these covered an area of 1,400 sq. metres. The arrivals included locomotives, dump cars, cranes, barges and dredgers. Men could not be recruited at the required rate and it was therefore proposed to import French convicts from New Caledonia, but local opposition put paid to this idea.

In the early days, the offices of the Company were located in separate buildings in Panama, but centralization under one roof was decided upon, in order to be able better to enforce the sanitary laws. The Grand Hotel on the Cathedral Plaza, built between 1874 and 1875, was bought and in December, 1881, it became the headquarters of the Company. During 1882 a great deal happened along the Panama Canal. There was a strike of workers, which resulted in an increase of 1.50 dollars per day. This was followed by the start of full-scale excavation in the Culebra Cut, celebrated by a banquet and ball in Panama City. During the same year, excavation was started at Mindi, Monkey Hill, Bas Obispo, Gorgona, Cristobal and Paraiso, but the dry season of 1882 passed with but little achieved.

The excavators were ready for use, but such was the lack of planned organization that no tracks were available to take

away the spoil that they were able to produce. Optimistic
forecasts were made of the great boom to be expected in
March, when from 3,000 to 4,000 men were to arrive. During
1882 there were also events of civic importance. The first
steam fire-engines arrived, and then the *Panama Star and
Herald* published editions in three languages. The first contained French, Spanish and English, and appeared on March
10th, 1882. This practice continued for more than twenty-two
years, extending into the period of American occupation. In
New York an office of the American Committee of the
Panama Canal Company was formed for the sale of securities
under the direction of Richard Thompson, ex-Secretary of
the Navy. Unfortunately, this venture was not successful
enough to be able to help the French at all, and they continued to rely on the private subscriptions received from
France.

Keen interest in the new canal was shown by Moses and
Henry Slaven, two brothers of San Francisco who, with
Prosper Herne, formed the American Contracting and Dredg-
ing Company with very meagre resources to back them.
Early in 1882 they were awarded a 2,000,000-dollar contract.
A medical corps was established by the Canal Company and
Sisters of St. Vincent de Paul arrived from France to nurse
the sick, a 200-bed hospital being established at Colon in
March, 1882. Supported on brick pillars extending out to sea
on the northern coastline, it received the full benefit of sea
breezes from the Caribbean. At Panama the Ancon Hospital
was started and the layout included admission and ward
buildings, canteen, dispensary, servants' hall, kitchen and
accommodation for the Sisters, who were authorized to
charge each patient 5 francs per day for their services. It
was dedicated on September 17th, 1882, by Bishop Paul of
Panama. Both vegetable and flower gardens were laid out
under the direction of the Mother Superior. In order to
protect the flowers from attacks by ants, waterways were
arranged around the flower-beds, and these became very
efficient breeding places for mosquitoes close to the un-

screened windows of the hospital! Many of the patients later became victims of mosquito-borne diseases.

By the end of 1882 all arrangements for cutting the canal were well under way. Many houses had been built for workers, a large number of exploratory borings completed, several lengths of railway lines laid near the working sites, and soundings taken in the sea close to the proposed sites for the ocean terminals. More than half the canal route had been cleared of jungle growth and the axis of the canal had been clearly marked by stakes. A contract was awarded to the American Contracting and Dredging Company of New York to dredge the channel on the Pacific side towards the cordillera. The difficult zone through the highlands was divided into small sections in order that the contractor responsible for each would be able to solve his own particular problems without much difficulty.

In spite of the praiseworthy efforts now being made by the French canal builders, American opposition was still strong. De Lesseps had to remain in France to campaign for still more money to keep things going, with the result that he knew practically nothing about progress of actual construction work. It is certain that his absence was one of the main causes that led to eventual French failure.

Admiral George Cooper of the United States Navy reported on March 2nd, 1883, that this project was so immense it could not be finished quickly, but that even if the French should fail for lack of funds, the work achieved would have been sufficient to make the Panama route superior to all other alternatives. Referring to its great promoter, Admiral Cooper said that the credit for the "design of the enterprise and of its energetic commencement would always be accorded to the French and especially to Ferdinand de Lesseps".

At this stage, when everyone waited impatiently for the great work to start, Gaston Blanchet, chief engineer of the contractors, died. His company had not realized what huge problems they had to face, and decided to withdraw from the work. On December 31st, 1882, they wrote to de Lesseps, asking for cancellation of the contract. De Lesseps had no other recourse than to accept, and having done so he at once appointed Jules Dingler as Director-General. Dingler was a brilliant engineer and had served as Chief Engineer of Bridges and Roads in France. Although his friends tried to dissuade him from going to work in such a bad climate as that of Panama, he scoffed at their warnings, and commented, "I am going to show them that only drunkards and the dissipated take the yellow fever and die there."

Accompanied by his family and Charles de Lesseps, son of Ferdinand, he sailed for Colon and arrived there on March 1st, 1883. His arrival was the excuse for a great banquet at the Grand Hotel, where the offices of the Company were at that time located. Then Dingler got down to the Herculean task of creating order out of chaos. He fully restored discipline to the whole enterprise, thereby incurring the dislike of those who did not wish to be regimented, and these malcontents proceeded to spread stories about extravagance. Nothing daunted, he organized work yards, studied the whole canal project and submitted a report on the sea-level canal, which was approved by the Superior Advisory Committee, ordering machinery he considered would be adequate for the task. Dingler's influence was described by Bunau-Varilla as "bold, loyal, scientific and stimulating". He adopted a system of small contracts and nearly thirty of these were granted, for which the Canal Company rented the necessary equipment at low rates. This system suffered from the problems of very frequent inspections and payments, and many lawsuits in the Colombian courts. However, he did get results even in the early years, when much of the excavation was done by hand.

It is interesting to review briefly Dingler's plan for the canal in order to compare it with other plans. All French plans used the metric system, and the length of his canal would have been 74 kilometres. Starting in Limon Bay, it followed the valley of the Chagres River about 45 kilometres to the Obispo branch. There it turned away from the Chagres and followed the Obispo towards the summit, thereafter the valley of the Rio Grande to the Pacific. The bottom width of this canal was to have been 22 metres (72 ft.) and the depth 9 metres (29·5 ft.). The flood waters of the Chagres River were to have been controlled by a dam at Gamboa and by lateral diversion channels. The total excavation on this route would have been 120,000,000 cub. metres (157,000,000 cub. yds.), or 45,000,000 cub. metres more than the volume estimated by the International Technical Commission in 1880.

He attacked the highest peaks of the central region in April with three excavators, seven locomotives, 70 dump cars and a force of 400 men in the Culebra Cut. Work proceeded apace, but soon there were misgivings about landslides and what slope ought to be adopted for the cuttings in order to avoid them. It was optimistically expected that the Culebra Cut would be finished by May, 1885.

At the continental divide the work was dry excavation, and at Colon and Panama dredging fleets were slowly working their way towards the centre of the canal. A great variety of machinery was at work, but a dismal sight was presented by an array of discarded plant that represented the mistakes and miscalculations of the first two years' work. The key to future success lay in the completion of the Culebra Cut.

In September, 1883, about 10,000 men were at work on the canal, and originally the promoters formed the idea of a single sea-level canal, which would be known as the Strait of Panama, but Dingler pointed out that there was a tidal range on the Pacific of about 20 ft., whereas that of the Atlantic was only about 1 ft. From this he concluded that the currents set up by the difference of levels of the two oceans during tide changes would be too dangerous for safe navigation. He therefore proposed that a tidal lock should be built at Panama to preserve the level from there to Colon, a plan which he estimated would save about 10,000,000 cub. metres of excavation. The locks were to be in three sections, one for exit, one for entrance, and one for repair, each 180 metres long and 25 metres in width.

A further public subscription realized another 171,000,000 francs to keep the job going, but with every new appeal to the public, money became harder to get. Towards the end of 1883 activity on the Isthmus was so great that transport facilities were overtaxed; the harbour at Colon was full of steamers and sailing vessels, laden with every class of material and machinery for the work. Deck space was inadequate in spite of the seven wharves at Colon, and many ships had to wait in the harbour for weeks before they could be unloaded. Yet contracts continued to be signed for excavation, and workers continued to be engaged, the Company providing materials for the contractors and houses for the workers. It was hoped that the canal would be completed by 1888, a prediction based on the assumption that during the first four dry months of 1884 the excavation would exceed that of the previous two years.

There were difficulties and tragedies during these early months of 1884. In January, the dredger *Prosper Herne* was destroyed by fire only a few days after arriving on the Isthmus, a loss that gravely retarded the dredging programme, but Slaven telegraphed the builders in New York to send down the next dredger and ordered an additional dredger as replacement. On the last day of the same month Louise Dingler, daughter of the chief engineer, contracted yellow fever and died after a brief illness. A month later, Jules Dingler's 20-year-old son showed signs of the same disease, and three days afterwards he too was dead. Then the daughter's young fiancé, who had come over with the family from France, also died from the fever. In spite of these tragedies, Dingler kept on working and Bunau-Varilla, who later worked under him, wrote, "These trials which might have shaken the reason of any man did not drive this hero one step out of the path of his duty to the task in hand." It was not until early June that Dingler left for France with his wife to consider the programme for 1885.

Unfortunately for the French promoters, the part played by mosquitoes in causing yellow fever was not discovered until many years later. Although the French Company had an excellent medical service and well-equipped hospitals they did not take those vital steps that would have prevented the spread of yellow fever and malaria—the eradication of the stegomyia and the anopheles, as well as the screening of houses. The French were ignorant of the imperative need for eliminating the breeding grounds for mosquitoes. Water troughs in the hospital grounds, and water placed under bedposts to keep off insects served as fertile breeding places near unsuspecting victims, so that patients would often contract yellow fever after arrival in hospital.

This appalling disease created an atmosphere of mystery and fear, yet Lieutenant Rodgers, writing on January 27th, 1884, reported that the climate thus far had not proved to be so fatal as expected in most of the canal sections, that employees appeared to be in fair health, and Europeans suffered more than the workers who were natives of the tropics.

It was at this stage that new rumours began circulating about the financial condition of the Panama Canal Company. A United States naval officer sent a report to the Secretary of State, dated June 2nd, 1884, stating that the company was in serious financial difficulties, with 60,000,000 dollars, representing about half the capital, already spent, apart from the 20,000,000 dollars paid for the Panama Railroad stock, and with half the estimated time for completion elapsed, yet only a thirtieth part of the work completed. This shrewd analyser concluded his report thus: "The completion of the Canal, according to present plans, is very doubtful. It certainly will require much more time and money than originally estimated."

De Lesseps optimistically replied to this adverse report that there was no reason for thinking that the work would not be completed in 1888. Owing to the efforts of Dingler, the excavation of 700,000 cub. metres in June, 1884, marked a new record of production. In spite of this, de Lesseps had once again to start a campaign for more money in August and September, but it was successful. Later the pessimistic forecasts of Lieutenant Brown, referred to above, found a supporter in Captain Bedford Pim of the Royal Navy, who had visited the Isthmus in October, 1884, "to set at rest conflicting reports . . . as to the progress of the Canal". On November 8th Pim submitted a report to the Secretary of the United States Navy as a "private and confidential" communication. Using de Lesseps' own estimates, which had been based on the completely different Suez work, he estimated that the excavation for the Panama Canal would require at least another fifteen years because of the nature of the soil, which ranged from alluvium to strata of hard rock and soil with large boulders, liable to heavy slides. There was the added difficulty of keeping some 10,000 men at work during the annual long rainy season, with the certainty that disease and death would take a heavy toll.

In 1884 there emerged the man, already referred to, who was to have a great influence on the history of the Panama Canal. His name was Philippe Bunau-Varilla, a young and ambitious man, who travelled to Panama with Jules Dingler and his wife on their return voyage to the Isthmus. On arrival, Bunau-Varilla was appointed division engineer in charge of the Culebra Cut and the Pacific slope division. Work at Culebra was in full swing, and during January, 1884, a mere 60,000 cub. metres were excavated, with another 25,000,000 cub. metres remaining to be extracted over a section two kilometres in length. At this rate it would have required a long time for completion, particularly when allowing for the inevitable slowing down during the rainy season. However, tracks had been laid and spoil dumps allocated.

Then further tragedy visited this unfortunate venture when Madame Dingler died of yellow fever. Dingler stuck to his post until June, his wife having died in the new year, and returned to France exhausted and alone, all his loved ones having been sacrificed for Panama. Maurice Hutin was appointed Director-General, but he also was attacked by yellow fever and returned to France in September. Young Bunau-

Varilla, at the early age of 26, became Director-General of what was at the time the largest engineering scheme in the world.

Equipment continued to arrive from abroad. *Dredger No. 19*, built by Lobnitz on the Clyde, completed its voyage of 88 days through the Straits of Magellan, a long voyage for a crew of only twenty men to make in such a clumsy craft. She was followed by another Slaven dredger, the eighth, named *The City of New York*. These dredgers were put to work in the jungle and soon proved their worth.

Bunau-Varilla made plans for excavating 1,400,000 cub. metres a month in January, 1886, but at Culebra the work went ahead very slowly, and on the Colon side of the job five excavators were extracting 300 cub. metres of spoil a day, but were held up for lack of trains to transport this output at the necessary rate. Huge slides occurred, and at Paraiso one slide carried away an entire hillside "almost intact across the Cut with the top surface unbroken, and with vegetation undisturbed".

Further rumours circulated about the financial troubles of the Company, and de Lesseps was having increasing difficulty in raising funds. In May, 1885, he wrote to the French Government, asking for authority to issue lottery bonds, a procedure which had been successful at Suez when that project was on the point of failure through lack of money. The Government hesitated, and Armand Rousseau, an eminent engineer, was appointed to conduct an inquiry on the Isthmus. These rumours stimulated interest in the United States once more, and in 1885 yet another United States naval officer, Lieutenant Kimball, visited the Isthmus, where he was received courteously by Bunau-Varilla and provided with all the necessary plans and information.

In his report, made on January 20th, 1886, he observed that much housing for workmen was under construction and a great deal of construction plant was available, but not of the right type. There were too few dredgers, and the French bucket excavating machines were too light and were stopped by large boulders. Moreover, too much of the work was being done by hand labour. There was a large turnover of labour because many men wanted to return home in order to spend the savings they had accumulated, and also because of inadequate medical care and a fear of political disturbance. In 1885 it was quite impossible to forecast a probable date of completion, in view of the many costly mistakes that had been made.

Many French workers died of yellow fever during the year, but malaria took an even greater toll. Kimball noted with obvious cynicism: "As for human life, that is always cheap." Later studies by Colonel Gorgas, the tropical disease expert, confirmed this view.

Experienced engineers knew that the solution lay in the construction of a high-level lock canal, both in order to reduce an enormous volume of excavation and to prevent slides. Yet it was still impossible to convince the obstinate de Lesseps of the fallacy of a sea-level canal, in spite of the alarming fact that in July, 1885, after several years of work, only about one-tenth of the estimated 120,000,000 cub. metres had been excavated. Nearly six years had elapsed since de Lesseps formally inaugurated the Panama Canal on January 1st, 1880, and he was now in his eighty-first year.

The report of Government Inspector Rousseau was submitted to the authorities in June, 1886. In it he stated that the scheme had gone so far that abandonment would mean disaster for the investors and a severe blow to French prestige throughout the Americas. By suggesting that the original plan should be modified and simplified he was obviously implying that a lock canal should be adopted. Another report by Jacquet also recommended that the sea-level idea should be abandoned and that a lock canal should be built. Leon Boyer went much further in his report, declaring bluntly that a sea-level canal could not possibly be completed within the time or according to the estimates of cost.

Although disappointed, de Lesseps still remained adamant in his mistaken opinions. He withdrew his lottery proposal and called a meeting of the stockholders on July 29th, 1886, at which he asked for authority to issue bonds. He explained at this meeting that the heaviest costs for the first years had been for organization and transport, but that the necessary plant had now been obtained and that future expenditure would be only for fuel and wages. Yet he did acknowledge at the same time that the higher charges on loans "must augment the cost of the canal". He added that an early meeting would be held by the Consulting Commission to consider "modifying the plan of construction".

Unfortunately, an early decision was not announced, so that investors were left in doubt of what was happening. He had asked for 600,000,000 francs, the 354,000,000 francs actually subscribed being a remarkable response by the public to a scheme that was being attacked by people who really did not know what they were talking about. The scandalous thing was that owing to the fees demanded by officials and to the operations of extortionists in France, only a mere 200,000,000 francs of the 354,000,000 was available to keep the work going.

During the campaign for funds in France, work on the Isthmus continued unabated. Early in 1886, Leon Boyer arrived with Charles de Lesseps to assume the post of Director-General, relieving Bunau-Varilla. Soon afterwards Bunau-Varilla, suffering from yellow fever, was carefully nursed by his friends and gradually recovered. Then he left for France.

Within a short time, Boyer was in conflict with Lillaz, a member of the firm of Baratoux, Letellier and Lillaz, at that time the only firm willing to undertake work for the Company. This firm had a contract for dredging in the Rio Grande and Pacific entrance to the canal. One of the dredgers sank, and Lillaz claimed reimbursement. Nervously upset by this setback, Lillaz was taken ill with yellow fever, and in his delirium he summoned Boyer for an appearance with him "before the Supreme Judge within eight days", and shortly afterwards he died. Boyer was overcome with distress at this tragedy. He attended the funeral, where he caught a chill, and next day showed signs of yellow fever. As he lay dying he thought mainly of the great enterprise on which he was working and his last words were, "Do not give up Panama." He was succeeded by Jacquet.

Work continued, with excavation exceeding the records of the same months in previous years. On January 1st, 1886, the total excavation from the beginning was nearly 18,500,000 cub. metres. For the whole of 1886 the total was about 11,700,000 cub. metres, a volume equal to about two-thirds of the entire previous canal excavation record and almost approaching the prediction of 12,000,000 cub. metres for 1886 that de Lesseps had made in 1885.

By the summer of 1886 work on the one-mile Culebra Cut had been in progress for about four years, the last two under an Anglo-Dutch Company. Rains, landslides, sickness, lack of transport, and equipment that was not powerful enough for the work which had to be done, allied to the laziness of the workers, delayed progress. The high peaks in the cutting had been removed, but little else. In the four years the average altitude of the lowest points had been reduced by only 12 ft. from the original 307 ft.—in other words, to 295 ft. above the bottom of the 30-ft. sea-level channel. At that painfully slow rate of 3 ft. a year the job would have required 99 years for completion.

The officials of the Panama Canal Company were extremely worried. Bunau-Varilla, recuperating from his illness in Paris, suggested to Charles de Lesseps as managing head of the Company that a special section of the Company should be allowed to take over the Culebra Cut under his direction, with full powers to select men from those who had been tested and found to be well qualified for this work. While acting as Director-General, Bunau-Varilla had raised the monthly volume of excavation from 720,000 cub. yds. in January, 1885, to 1,400,000 in January, 1886. The Board of Directors did not approve of this idea and considered that the work should be continued on a contract basis.

It was then suggested to Bunau-Varilla that he himself should form a company to take over the work in Culebra. Liking the idea of being a hero, he gladly accepted this proposal. He therefore resigned from the Panama Canal Company in September, and proceeded to Panama, where he lived in a small house alongside the Cut so that he could watch the progress of the work. During the French effort in 1887 the most active stage was reached, with 26 excavators at work and 42 locomotives drawing 2,000 dump cars over a network of tracks carrying the spoil to nearby dumps.

Then the rains came. The vast mass of Cucuracha (Cockroach) on the east bank south of Gold Hill began to creep slowly but surely into the Cut at the rate of 18 in. a year. Layers of clay, separated by mixtures of sand, alluvial deposits and conglomerate, made slippery by water seeping down through them, moved simply as a result of the lack of balance of natural forces caused by the excavation. The French engineers saw a grave portent in these slides, realizing that they probably signalled the end of a sea-level canal idea. Excavation at Cucuracha was stopped, the slides came to rest, and the engineers made a close study of the new problems created by the slides and of methods for overcoming them.

Charles de Lesseps, accompanied by other Company officials, arrived at Colon from Paris early in March, wishing to check the local situation by personal inspection, which was what his father should have done on many more occasions. He realized the impossibility of completing the sea-level canal in the time limit given, and was fully aware that a lock canal would be the only possible solution. It was too late already, however, because the dwindling resources of the Company ruled out any hope of continuing the sea-level idea. But whilst plans were being awaited, work at Culebra was pushed ahead.

During 1887 the average level was lowered 10 ft., as compared with 3 ft. during the previous year; in 1888 it was lowered 20 ft., bringing the level to 235 ft. above sea level when the works were stopped. Bunau-Varilla estimated that the level would be lowered 30 ft. in 1889 and 50 ft. in 1890, leaving only 15 ft. to be lowered in 1891 to bring the level to 140 ft., which was required for the 30-ft. depth with a summit level of 170 ft. above sea level. He believed that if this key problem were solved in 1888, the excavation could be completed within two and a half years of completion, and the canal would be open for traffic in 1891.

During these critical months there was much activity in Paris, where critics of the canal were trying to persuade de Lesseps to alter the plans so that the job could be finished in a reasonable time. A meeting of the Superior Advisory Committee was held in January, 1887, to consider the subject, and it at once passed the whole matter to a subcommission not due to meet until September. No public announcement of the change of plans was made, in spite of the fact that all experts, and even the commission headed by Charles de Lesseps, saw all too clearly that it was impossible to carry out the plan of a sea-level canal. The public was kept in ignorance of the true position, and it is probable that if they had been educated in the right way about the whole scheme public confidence might have been maintained and further funds raised for carrying on the work.

The very opposite was done. On January 18th, 1887, de Lesseps wrote to the stockholders of the Company that he was convinced a sea-level canal could be built, as determined by the Paris Congress in 1879. However, he then announced that he had instructed the Superior Advisory Commission to report on the plans for a lock canal already submitted and also to examine other ideas for completing the waterway with minimum delay, yet allowing a sea-level canal to be built eventually.

More and much stronger rumours about financial difficulties were circulating and by July, 1887, there were reports of the impending bankruptcy of the Company. Landslides, failure to control the Chagres River and the increasing difficulty of raising more money intensified the rumours still further. The stockholders met in Paris on July 21st, 1887, with the Emperor of Brazil in attendance. A report by de Lesseps showed he doubted that it would be possible to open the canal in 1889, and he had to put forward further inducements for investors to support his scheme. The new subscription for 100,000,000 dollars announced for July 26th was at a discount of 57½ per cent, yet it yielded only 42,500,000 dollars. With a mere 20,000,000 dollars reported as left in the treasury, this relatively small sum would not last long.

At first the despatches from Paris reaching Panama stated that the loan had been subscribed in full. In fact the final result showed that 114,000,000 francs were produced, representing only two-thirds of the loan, but de Lesseps considered that this would be sufficient for carrying on the work. Another stockholders' meeting was called for September 25th, at which the change of plan due to force of circumstances was announced. De Lesseps stated that a further 150,000,000 dollars would be required to open the Canal, of which 60 kilometres of the total 74 had been completed on time.

On November 15th de Lesseps sent out two letters. One was to the French Minister of Finance, once more requesting authority to issue 600,000,000 francs of lottery bonds to cover expenses from January 1st, 1888, to the assumed opening of the canal in about 1890. A letter to the shareholders announced that the services of the famous Gustave Eiffel, builder of the Tower that bears his name, was to be asked to design the locks. De Lesseps referred to the bitter attacks which had been made on the Company, and included false letters, telegrams, circulars and pamphlets, all designed to reduce confidence and produce a fall in the value of the shares on the Bourse.

Work on the lock canal started at Pedro Miguel on January 15th, 1888, and at San Pablo in February. The same general route was followed, with a summit level 170 ft. above sea level. This placed the summit level above the flood waters of the Chagres so high that it was necessary to feed the summit level by machinery. There were to be ten locks, five on each slope, and all sited on compact rock. The lock gates were to be made in Europe under the direction of Eiffel, using a modified design of the lock gates he had prepared for the Nicaragua Canal.

In May, 1888, there were 5,000 men working on the ten lock sites, and work was being pushed ahead by night and day. At this time sections of the work were nearing completion, and as the year drew to its close, Culebra Cut showed remarkable progress. In July about 5,000,000 cub. metres remained to be excavated in a short yet difficult section. Between 2,500 and 3,000 men worked here in a cutting that was lit at night by electricity. With 800 dump cars and 54 locomotives operating over 37 kilometres of track at the rate of 100 muck trains a day, the scene of activity was intensified by the sight of 23 steam excavators at work, keeping the trains supplied.

In Paris, a meeting of shareholders was called by de Lesseps when the Government refused to authorize lottery bonds. His audience consisted mainly of small investors to whom a collapse at Panama would be a personal disaster. Yet de Lesseps appealed for confidence and was backed up by his son, who advised the shareholders to hold their shares; they authorized a loan of 340,000,000 francs. It was estimated that the cost to complete the canal would be 654,000,000 francs: 254,000,000 for excavating, 125,000,000 for locks and masonry, 15,000,000 francs for reservoirs and summit level supply. The cost for materials was estimated at 50,000,000 francs, and 210,000,000 for general purposes. With the loan of 340,000,000 and the 260,000,000 already authorized, in addition to 110,000,000 on hand, there would then be a margin of 56,000,000 francs.

Friends of the Company in the French Parliament appealed to members not to abandon this great national enterprise, as a result of which a lottery law was passed by the Chamber of Deputies on April 28th, and by the Senate early in June, 1888, after long debates in both houses. De Lesseps stepped up his campaign, and on one occasion he addressed the

Above, King's Bridge, Old Panama, crossed by conquerors bearing their stolen gold and treasures from the South *en route* to Spain, is the only remaining evidence of the "Gold Trail"; *below*, the reception of M. de Lesseps in Cathedral Place on the occasion of his inspection of the Canal works in 1886

A deep cutting through the mountains, Culebra

A large locomotive dredger, *Las Cascadas*. These views of the Canal works
in 1887 are both reproduced from *The Graphic*

Topographical Society of France; wearing his Legion of Honour ribbon, he read an illustrated paper in which he claimed that the canal would be opened in 1890. Pointing to his photographs, he said, "The sun is our best collaborator, for he furnishes to photography the means of refuting the calumnies of our adversaries." But it needed more than this kind of help to rescue the scheme from disaster.

Enemies of the canal did not wait until the day of issue of the lottery. Indeed, three days before the date they dumped Panama Canal shares on the market to depress the price, and on the day of issue they even went to the dastardly length of telegraphing false news that de Lesseps was dead. Yet in spite of these unscrupulous attacks, out of the 2,000,000 bonds issued, 800,000 were subscribed by 350,000 people. This was still a dismal failure and caused the price of the shares to drop considerably. Baron Jacques de Reinach had advised that the issue should be limited to only 660,000 bonds, but this was not allowed by the bank, who insisted that all the 2,000,000 bonds should be offered at one time. Bunau-Varilla went so far as to blame this failure of financing for the collapse of the Old Panama Canal Company.

Then came another heavy blow. De Lesseps had completed plans for the formation of a new company, when the Government bill providing for three months' postponement of payments on its bills came up for a vote on December 15th and was rejected by 256 votes to 181 in the Chamber. Ten minutes after this vote had been taken, a reporter called on de Lesseps to tell him about the rejection; the old man was pale and speechless at the news. Placing a handkerchief to his lips, he cried, "*C'est impossible. C'est indigne!*" He would not believe that the French Chamber could sacrifice the interests of the Nation, and went on to lament that this would be a triumph for his enemies and a disaster to the flag.

There were scenes of wild confusion in the offices of the Company, the hall crowded with subscribers and women weeping at the loss of their savings. Some were facing complete ruin, and all were waiting for the appearance of

3

Ferdinand de Lesseps. In an effort to restore their confidence, he mounted a platform and shouted above the roar, "My friends! Your subscriptions are safe. Our adversaries are confounded, and we now have no need of financiers. You have saved yourselves by your own exertions. The canal will be made!" The crowd relieved their pent-up emotions by a round of cheers, and even pressed in upon de Lesseps to shake his hands, women in tears trying to kiss his clothing. Although more money was subscribed even at this stage, the subscribers were disillusioned when they found that the Canal could be saved only by Government intervention and help; de Lesseps had withdrawn, leaving control to temporary managers.

From Washington came very bad news for those who had hoped that help would come from the French Government. Senator Edmunds of Vermont introduced a Joint Resolution in the Senate on December 19th, 1888, expressing "serious concern with disapproval" of any European Government's connexion with "the construction or control of any ship-canal across the Isthmus of Darien or across Central America". He declared that this connexion would be "injurious to the just rights and interests of the United States and as a menace to their welfare". The President was requested to "communicate this expression of the views of Congress to the governments of Europe". Yet even in spite of this very powerful opposition, a meeting of 4,000 bondholders passed a resolution of confidence in de Lesseps, even expressing their willingness to forgo interest payments until the Canal could be opened for traffic.

Nevertheless, there was profound depression throughout France when this news was received, and the Canal became a subject for general conversation. Although the public in Panama assumed that this crisis had become a disaster, the contractors pushed on with the work. A French warship was rushed to Panama in anticipation of disorders, and two were expected to arrive from the United States. Word then came to Artigue and Donderegger, the contractors, that they were to stop work. This meant that some 2,500 men were idle in the Culebra Cut, yet order still prevailed in spite of a feeling of general alarm.

Strenuous efforts were being made, even at this late stage, to save the scheme in Paris. President Slaven of the American Contracting and Dredging Company was in daily conference with de Lesseps, and meetings of bondholders were held all over the country. Yet in spite of all these efforts, the movement to try and form a new company was frustrated. The last meeting of shareholders was held in January, 1889, when it was resolved to appoint a judicial receiver, and on February 4th the Old Panama Canal Company was dissolved and Joseph Brunet was appointed as liquidator. The tragedy was that when de Lesseps had released his controlling hand on the enterprise, there was nobody big enough to take his place.

Shops were closed in Panama. Dredgers were left where they had been working; excavators, locomotives and all kinds of rolling-stock were placed in sidings; villages lost their populations and the unemployed workers drifted away. The new Colon Hospital became an almshouse run by the Catholic Sisters. The jungle closed in upon the deserted works. In the middle of the investigation, Brunet was taken ill and had to call in Achille Monchicourt to help him and act as co-receiver. Then Brunet resigned, and died soon afterwards.

The Commission reported on May 5th, 1890, that a lock canal could be completed in eight years, that the plant on the Isthmus was adequate for the work that remained to be done, and that the estimated cost of completion would be 580,000,000 francs. However, it was recommended that the most careful study should be made before starting work again. The liquidation dragged on from 1891 to 1894, the only important work accomplished on the site being the collection of hydraulic data on the régime of the Chagres.

In France the Panama affair precipitated a political crisis. The Government, responding to popular pressure, decided to prosecute de Lesseps and those responsible for the débâcle.

There was another tragedy with the suicide of Baron de Reinach. Ferdinand de Lesseps, his son and Eiffel were indicted for alleged corruption but mercifully Ferdinand escaped that fate; sitting at home with his family, he was reported as having a state of mind "from which there is no recovery"; he died on December 7th, 1894, at the age of 89. Charles de Lesseps and Eiffel were both sentenced to five years' imprisonment, but the sentences were never executed. Charles lived until 1923.

The original Wyse Concession was due to expire in 1893, and there was a risk that the French would lose their franchise. As a result of the favourable report of the investigators, Monchicourt asked Wyse to travel once again to Bogotá, where he succeeded in obtaining a two-year extension of the concession on December 10th, 1890. Monchicourt was worn out by his strenuous work and died on March 14th, 1894, being succeeded by J. P. Gautron of the New Panama Canal Company which was organized on October 21st, 1894, under the title of "Compagnie Nouvelle du Canal de Panama". One of the conditions imposed by the Old Company was the appointment of a Technical Committee to put forward a definite plan for a canal.

The New Panama Canal Company was only a small organization with a capital of 650,000 shares of 100 francs each, of which 50,000 paid-up shares were assigned to Colombia; this left a capital of only 60,000,000 francs, a sum far too small with which to start works on a large scale. On December 9th, 1894, the first detachment of employees for the New Company sailed from France. This included a new Director-General, Vautard, and twenty employees. Work started again in the vital Culebra Cut, for this excavation had to be done whether the canal was to be a sea-level one or a lock type. The working force grew from 700 men to a maximum of more than 4,000 in 1897.

The New Company was quick to appoint a Comité Technique, composed of men with the highest professional qualifications. One of the members was General Abbot, an

American officer who had made a detailed study of the Chagres. This Comité arrived at Panama in February, 1896, and at once set to work on a plan for the best method of continuing the work. It was at about this time that the Spanish-American War broke out, and the spectacular cruise of the American ship *Oregon* around Cape Horn had a decisive influence on the subsequent demand of the United States for complete control of the Isthmian Canal.

The Comité Technique completed their plans on November 16th, 1898, a fateful date because it was exactly three years before the Isthmian Canal Commission was to recommend a Nicaragua Canal. In these new plans the Canal route remained substantially the same as before. There were to be two levels, one an artificial Lake Bohio about 61·5 ft. above sea level and approached from the Atlantic level through a double-flight lock; there was also to be a summit level at 97·5 ft. above sea level, and also reached by a double flight of locks from Lake Bohio at Obispo. The descent to the Pacific was to be through three locks—a single-stage lock at Paraiso, a double-flight one at Pedro Miguel and a single-chamber one at Miraflores. This canal was to have a bottom width of 98 ft. and a depth of 29·5 ft. Each lock was to be 738 ft. long, 82 ft. wide, and about 32 ft. deep. Cost was estimated at about 101,850,000 dollars, and the summit level was to be fed from Madden Lake. A second plan, with Lake Bohio as the summit level and fed directly by the Chagres, was submitted as an alternative scheme.

These plans were based on meeting the problems of controlling the flow of the Chagres and minimizing the excavation in the Culebra Cut. The New Company, well aware that the only chance of seeing a return on its capital lay in holding on until the United States Government should take charge of the Isthmus, sent a copy of the Comité Technique report to President McKinley, which he received on December 2nd, 1898. During its latter years the Company confined its efforts to the volume of excavation necessary for holding the concession.

It would be a great mistake to minimize the French effort, for it was indeed tremendous; the lessons they learnt with such pain and anguish were of the utmost value to the United States when eventually American engineers completed the Canal. It was also the French effort that pioneered the route of the first waterway across the Isthmus, and for this French explorers richly deserve a place in the history of the project.

The Old Panama Canal Company, formed by the French with French capital, had started construction of a sea-level canal without having investigated the problems of being prepared to meet and overcome them. In short, they went into their own project with immense enthusiasm and unbelievable ignorance. The error of a sea-level canal, under the conditions of those days when earth-moving and excavating machinery had not been developed to the pitch necessary for a scheme of this size, was realized far too late to be able to redeem it.

Although there had been corruption in high places in France, the behaviour of both de Lesseps and his son Charles was perfectly honourable, although they paid dearly for their lack of technical knowledge and the dislike that Ferdinand had for engineers. There were also instances of incompetence, but the ability and experience of those French engineers who did take a prominent part in the work were perfectly adequate for the task.

Malaria and yellow fever caused much suffering and many deaths, but they were not the prime cause of French failure. The basic reason was clearly the obstinate refusal of de Lesseps to follow the sound advice of Godin de Lépinay at the Paris Congress in 1879, allied with the decision to build a sea-level canal without being fully aware of what this vast project would entail. When the French Company was at last convinced of the necessity for a lock canal, it was too late to avoid a crash. By then money had run out and there was no source to which the Company could turn for more support as soon as it became a target for political attack in France.

By the year 1888, the engineering problems of a canal had been largely solved. There were 14,000 men on the payroll in

September of that year, and excavation was proceeding apace at a rate of about 1,000,000 cub. metres per month, with a remaining estimated volume of 23,700,000 cub. metres to be removed to complete the canal, which would have enabled a completion date to be fixed at some time in 1891. Yet here again the tragedy was that if the Canal had been completed as planned in 1888, it would have been obsolete even before the date of opening!

Some interesting information about the plant employed by French engineers during their long struggle to build the Panama Canal has been given by Mr. Williams, an American engineer who visited the works in 1888, in a paper presented to the American Society of Civil Engineers.[1]

He visited three Scotch dredgers, of the type shown in Fig. 1, which he saw at work in the Bay of Panama, but their output of dredged material was only 200 cub. yds. per hour at the time because they had encountered coral rock on the sea bed. These dredgers were designed for a normal output of from 2,000 to 3,000 cub. metres per day of 12 hours. They were self-propelled and steamed from Scotland to Colon and to Panama, passing around the Horn. The steam dredging machinery had an output of 200 h.p., the horizontal engines transmitting power to a crankshaft on which was mounted a sprocket wheel, motion from the latter having been transmitted to the upper tumbler by an endless chain. In heavy work the teeth of these sprockets frequently broke.

The ladder over which the dredging buckets worked was made in one section, and had to be very heavily constructed in order to give it the necessary strength. Mr. Williams comments that if this component had been in two parts it would have been lighter and therefore require less power to move it either up or down. He goes on to say that this design of dredger was more suitable for deep-sea work than for canal excavation. Each vessel drew from 7 to 8 ft. and consumed 6 tons of coal in a working shift of 12 hours.

[1] "Plant and Material of the Panama Canal" by W. P. Williams, *Journal Am. Soc. C.E.*, Vol. XIX, December 1888.

1. *A Scotch bucket dredger*

The French dredger shown in Fig. 2 was the main instrument of underwater excavation during French operations. The most widely used size had a length of 100 ft. and a beam of 30 ft., drawing 7 ft. of water. Hulls and machinery of each dredger were shipped in convenient sections from France to Colon and were then transhipped at different points along the line where they were to be used. The cost of each vessel was about 115,000 dollars at Colon, but this did not include the cost of erection, which was so expensive at Panama that some engineers estimated it to be as much as 35 per cent of the original value. The tower was quite low, the elevation of the hopper below the upper tumbler being only 20 ft. above water level. The ladder was in one section, and could be varied in length in accordance with the nature of the work being undertaken. The dredging buckets were made of iron, wrought in one piece, the links forming an integral part of each bucket. Power for dredging was provided by a three-cylinder vertical steam-engine with gear transmission.

A method of hydraulic discharge of dredged material used at Tavernilla was seen by Mr. Williams, and at the same place he also saw equipment for this process under construction for use as auxiliary plant for a French dredger. It consisted of an iron barge, 60 ft. long and with a beam of 35 ft., having three large horizontal steam-engines mounted in the stern; each had a piston of 20 in. diameter with a stroke of 3 ft. Each piston rod was elongated and connected directly with the piston of a water pump, the three pumps receiving their supply of water from alongside the hull; this water, under high pressure, was forced forward to the hoppers. There were two hoppers in each barge, with large cylinders and a small bottle-neck opening, receiving the material discharged from the hopper of the dredger. This material was well lubricated by water discharged in the hopper through two 9-in. diameter pipes.

At the neck of the hopper there were two iron gratings, placed at right angles to each other, thereby disintegrating the material falling into the hopper. There was a 20-in.

3*

2. *A French dredger*

diameter outlet at the bottom of the hopper, and there were three pressure water pipes: two at the bottom, and on the quarter opposite the outlet pipe, extending the stream of water so that it would strike the material and drive it towards the outlet. There was another pipe entering from above the outlet and inclined in a downward direction. The three streams of water thereby produced met at a common point, the outlet for the material. This imparted a considerable force to the material, depending on the power of the engine.

This arrangement filled the full diameter of the discharge pipe with a mixture of earth and water, with all air excluded, so that the only outlet for the material would be through the bottom of the hopper and then out on shore through a pipeline supported by pontoons. The system was claimed to have several advantages, one being that material did not come into contact with pump components, and another that in extreme cases when gravel had to be excavated the gratings were removed, so that all material passed through the hopper when its size did not exceed the diameter of the discharge pipe.

For dredging high banks, where the discharge had to be at some appreciable distance both horizontally and vertically from the dredger, practical experience proved that this was the best system to use. For harbour work, when not affected by surf or ocean swell, the bucket type of dredger working with hydraulic discharge through a floating pipeline was considered preferable. In sand dredging, the buckets were operated at such a speed that the sand would fill 15 per cent of the pipe diameter, the remaining 85 per cent being water, which had to be at a higher pressure than for dredging in clay, because unless the sand was kept moving at a uniform rate it tended to form obstructions in the pipe. Because the clay tended to form balls with sand, gravel and other obstacles it had to be disintegrated before passing through the discharge pipe. As these balls rolled through the pipe they hardened, and Mr. Williams stated that he had seen lumps nearly three-quarters the diameter of the pipe, blocking the steady flow of water and dredged material.

3. *A Belgian dredger*

The Belgian type of dredger (Fig. 3) was similar to the French design, and was fitted with the same kind of power transmission system. The cost was less, however, because the vessel was lighter, and Mr. Williams was told that a Belgian dredger could be landed on the Isthmus for 90,000 dollars. The charge for erection varied widely, whether this was done at Colon or at some more distant point, where workshops and living quarters imposed an extra charge. The dredging crews varied from 30 to 40 men. In the case of French, Belgian and Scotch dredgers there was only a day shift at work, on account of the danger involved in operating hopper barges liable to run aground through faulty navigation on their passage to and from the dumping ground at night. During his visit, Mr. Williams related how he inspected a large consignment of the Ingersoll type of rock drills which were shipped to the Société de Travaux Publiques for use at Bas Obispo and Emperador. These machines were used for only a few days owing to the lack of an adequate number of skilled foremen to instruct the native workmen in their operation. As a result, all this valuable machinery was abandoned. In his paper Mr. Williams remarks: "I did not see any machine drills in operation in crossing over the whole line, and the most modern plant which has accomplished such wonderful work upon our New York Aqueduct has been side-tracked at Panama for reasons dependent upon labor."

From the above remarks we get some idea of the many problems that confronted the pioneering French engineers. According to Mr. Williams, the French drilling machines proved to be cumbersome for every type of work and for uneven ground. A platform car, mounted on four wheels, supported a horizontal steam boiler with an output of 15 h.p. Four rock drills, 3 ft. apart, were supported on an upright frame and the drills were raised or lowered by a ratchet and pinion attachment within the frame. A circular motion was transmitted to each drill by a shaft from the main engine fitted with a bevel gear. The drill was a boring type of machine rather than one operating with a reciprocating

action. The contact between the drill and the rock was maintained by the operator with a hand-operated mechanism, and this demanded a certain amount of skill.

In order to work the machine, a track of 5-ft. gauge had to be constructed on the area to be excavated by blasting. When the requisite number of shotholes had been drilled, the machine was run back along the track, which was lifted, and the explosive charges were then fired electrically. This process was expensive because tracks had to be laid and removed for each round of shots. Moreover, the drilling machine could work efficiently only on comparatively level ground, whereas an Ingersoll machine could be stationed on hilly and uneven ground, drilling vertically, upwards or downwards, or at an angle; no tracks were needed for this machine, which could be transported from place to place by manpower.

A submarine drill was successfully used by the French canal builders at each end of the line. A drill of this type was built at Colon; the hull of the boat in which it was mounted was 50 ft. long and had a beam of 20 ft., being propelled by steam-engines that also powered the drilling equipment. In the forward part of this vessel there was an open square, 20 ft. long and 15 ft. wide, over which was erected a travelling frame carrying the drill. The frame had a fore-and-aft motion and ran on tracks at each side of the boat; there was a battery of four drills.

A telescopic watertight pipe was lowered from the frame of the drill and driven down into the bed of the channel, the drills working within this watertight sleeve. After the four drills had made the holes, the explosive charges were inserted and wired, the wires being made fast to the deck. The drill frame was then moved forward on its tracks for a few feet and four more shotholes were drilled and loaded. The hull was controlled by fore-and-aft guys and side guys, whereby the work was limited to a certain area. The boat was withdrawn to a safe distance while the shots were fired. This was the method used for blasting the coral rock at

4. *An American-type Hercules dredger, working 8 metres above sea level*

Panama and Colon, which was then removed by dredging. The cost of the barge was from 3,000 to 5,000 dollars and the drilling equipment cost about 2,000 dollars.

In addition to the shotholes of small diameter used for rock blasting, large shafts were used for attacking formations of volcanic origin which was porous, and in which a charge tended to blow out through the different strata. A hole 1 metre square was excavated to a depth of 10 metres, and at the bottom of this shaft two chambers, 1 metre square and 2 metres long, were extended in opposite directions. Both chambers and shaft were filled with barrels of powder and dynamite. At a depth of 5 metres below the surface, cement was used as a filling, and after this had set hard there was practically a solid mass of artificial stone from ground level to the top of the explosive charge. Several of these shafts were made and the charges were fired simultaneously. A vast mass of rock was thereby loosened, which could be attacked by workmen armed with picks and shovels. The method was highly successful in soft rock, but costly in that it required a large quantity of explosive.

At the time of Mr. Williams's visit to the canal works, the shotholes for the big excavations were generally drilled by means of the simple churn type of drill, from 6 to 18 ft. long, and of different diameters. The men were paid at the rate of 25 to 30 cents per lineal metre of depth for holes from 6 to 8 ft. deep or less; where the holes exceeded 8 ft. in depth, the payment was from 30 to 45 cents per linear metre, the quality of the rock regulating the schedule of prices to a considerable extent. These prices included allowance for the labour involved in charging and firing the shotholes, the contractor providing the material. The cost of transporting the cumbersome mechanical rock drills, to which we have already referred, ruled them out in favour of the simpler churn drills which the untrained men understood and with which they did achieve satisfactory results. Figs. 4 and 5 show American dredgers and Fig. 6 shows French equipment at work in the Culebra Cut.

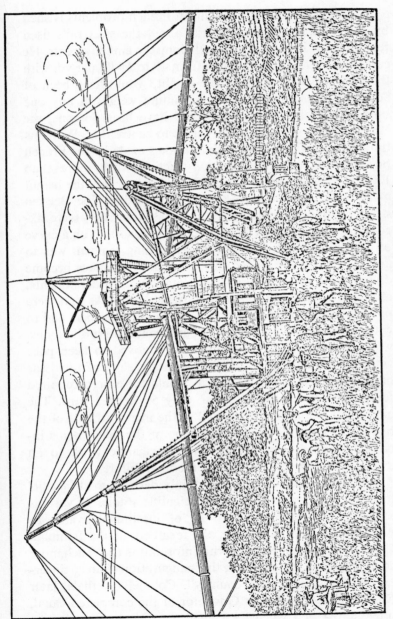

5. *The American Hercules dredger* City of Paris

A further interesting sidelight on French problems is shed by Mr. Williams in his remarks about the steel rails used for transport in the cuttings and along the embankments. He considered that a rail weighing from 40 to 55 lb. per yd. with the base equal in width to the height, would have been of adequate strength, where the maximum weight at any one time of a French excavator would have been 36 tons, the sleepers being spaced at 2 ft. centre to centre. Mr. Williams thought one of the most costly mistakes made by the French builders was to order for construction work more than 120,000 tons of steel rails weighing 70 lb. per yd., the height of the rail largely exceeding the base width. The Belgian steam locomotives employed weighed 30 tons; they were six-coupled engines with a wheelbase of 13 ft., so that on a curve of more than eight degrees the overturning moment was so great that the rails tended to spread and the spikes become drawn from the sleepers. This caused many derailments, more particularly on the vital construction tracks that were not adequately ballasted, so that the rail and sleepers had to withstand the whole load. On embankments and spoil dumps, where the track had to be frequently moved to keep pace with the progress of excavation, a larger gang of men was necessary for track shifting than would have been required for dealing with rails weighing only 50 lb. per yard. The additional labour charge, added to the increased cost of the heavier section of rail, was only one of the many items increasing French expenditure on this gigantic work to an extent that contributed towards the final failure.

The New Canal Company certainly derived great benefits from its predecessor, and made scientific studies of various aspects which were later to be of inestimable value to American engineers. In fact, the members of the Isthmian Canal Commission regarded this information as "much more complete than is usual before the inauguration of an engineering enterprise in a new country". Colonel Goethals, later Chief Engineer and then Governor of the completed canal, often stated that when he wanted accurate information he

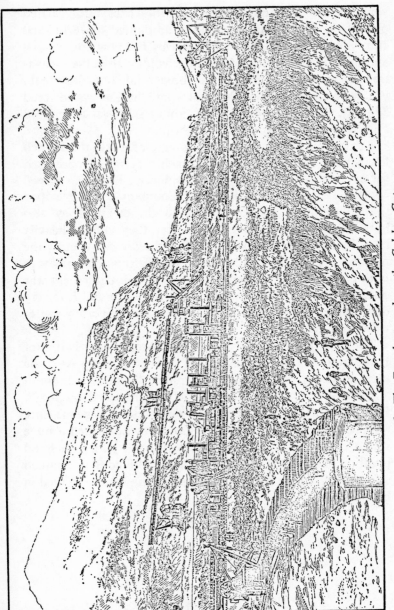

6. *The French at work on the Culebra Cut*

would turn to the French plans. The total excavation carried out by the two French companies amounted to 78,146,960 cub. yds., of which 11,403,409 was by the new company— and that alone represented a greater volume than the excavation for the Suez Canal. Of the above total, 18,646,000 cub. yds. were removed from Culebra, where the Cut was lowered 333·5 ft. to a high point 193 ft. above sea level near Gold Hill, peaks and ridges having been removed.

Apart from this considerable volume of work, the French left behind them buildings and machinery which were used for many years by the American engineers. They also gained control of the Panama Railroad Company and developed the railway itself as an adjunct to the canal. They also initiated a very fine hospital service but they suffered heavily from ignorance of the part played in disease carrying by the mosquito. They also made the most unfortunate mistakes in both planning and financing the work. Their equipment was certainly too light and inadequate for the job and it is very doubtful whether anyone else would have done any better with such machinery.

The most pathetic figure in all this sorry history is that of Ferdinand de Lesseps. Instead of giving him help when he most needed it, the French Government "abandoned him in a cowardly way, and then shamefully trampled on him". Four years after he died, as if to compensate in some measure for their behaviour, the French Government erected a huge statue of the Canal Builder at Port Said, with one hand pointing towards the East. Later on the United States named a fort guarding the Atlantic entrance to the Panama Canal in his honour.

4

POLITICAL MANŒUVRES

THE United States Government took a keen interest in the construction of the Panama Canal from the very outset of the French attempt, and with the failure of the French Company in 1899 a Commission headed by General Walker was sent to Panama. The result was that the U.S. Government acquired all the assets, construction equipment and partially completed works of the French Company for a sum of 40,000,000 dollars, a purchase price claimed to include the concessions previously granted by the Colombian Government, together with all other fixed assets on site. The final winding up of the French companies was then transferred to Paris, and the U.S. Government thereafter took charge of all future activities as far as the construction and health services of the Canal were concerned.

Those who have not lived in or visited the two areas where de Lesseps carried out his great works will find it difficult to appreciate why he succeeded so brilliantly at Suez and yet failed so dismally at Panama. Lewin, having been employed in the defence of both canals during and since the Second World War, travelling by air and land in Egypt and Panama, is quite convinced that the greatest enemy contributing to de Lesseps' failure was uncontrollable disease.

When de Lesseps returned to Egypt to carry out his Suez Canal project, Mohamad Said Pasha had become the Khedive; he was the Sultan's viceroy and the ruler of Egypt. De Lesseps at once revived the friendship that began when he was French Consul at Alexandria and Cairo. He had always been a great diplomat and soon convinced Said of the benefits to be derived from his project, with the result that his concession was quickly granted and ratified in Constantinople. In forming his Suez Canal Company, he made Mohamad Said Pasha the *major individual* shareholder, with the added advantage of being the major dividend earner in the operation of the Canal!

By this shrewd diplomatic move he was assured not only of the goodwill of the ruler of Egypt, but also of the full protection of the Canal as soon as it was in operation. Mohamad Said Pasha died before the Canal was opened, and seven years after his death his successor sold all his inherited holdings in the Canal to the British Government. This astute deal was negotiated by Disraeli with the financial backing of the Rothschilds, which explains why it later became necessary for the British Government to maintain a military garrison in Egypt for the defence of the Canal.

When de Lesseps turned his genius to the Panama problem, he had to go to Bogotá to negotiate his first concession for cutting a canal through the then remote province of Panama, and once more his diplomacy was successful, but he certainly had to pay a very high price. Later he obtained an extension of time, when he negotiated with the Colombian Government for payment to be made partly in shares, which suggests that both he and his advisers realized there was a great difference between the Egyptian Khedive—regarded in his day as a fine character—and the Colombian Government then established in Bogotá. This difference is even more marked when it is borne in mind that the province of Panama was at that time the most remote and neglected part of Colombia. It was very sparsely populated by Indian tribes, armed only with bows and arrows and poisoned darts. Indeed, such tribes still exist today quite a short distance from the Panama Canal Zone.

When the United States Government acquired all the French assets and concessions in Panama, they were also fully informed of de Lesseps' diplomatic success at Suez. They also had detailed information of his disastrous failure at Panama, briefly outlined in the last chapter. The advisers to the U.S. Government realized that they could not reopen any of the construction works, nor risk any more deaths from disease until: (a) they had assured the defence of the Canal if and when it was completed and in operation, and (b) they were convinced that every effort known to medical science was being made to eliminate disease, or at least control it.

After taking over from the French, the United States Government at once began diplomatic negotiations with the Colombian Government in Bogotá to secure complete control over the zone of land and water extending for five miles on each side of the Canal route, and for a distance of three miles seawards at each end. American experts set out to determine the best methods of coping with the prevalent diseases before any actual work was started.

There is little record of United States-Colombian negotiations during the period from 1899 to 1903, except that the U.S. Minister in Bogotá and the Colombian Minister in Washington were both actively engaged in such negotiations. At the same time the foremost medical authorities were undertaking a concentrated scientific study of the sanitation of the whole area. Much was accomplished by the spraying of oil on stagnant water, wherever drainage was impracticable, in order to eliminate the mosquitoes, which were the greatest carriers of disease.

Early in 1903 an agreement was signed in Washington whereby the Colombian Government granted the absolute rights requested by the United States Government, yet after nearly four years of negotiations the Colombian Government still declined to ratify this agreement. President Theodore Roosevelt was now the Chief Executive of the United States and a complete examination of all the factors leading up to this impasse was submitted to him. In his own summary of the position he remarked that there had not been a Government in Bogotá for over fifty years which had completed its constitutional period of four years, before being thrown out by a revolution or other political unrest. Thus there was little likelihood of a stable Government in Colombia in the near future. The province of Panama had once been an independent state for a limited period, but the present position was that the Panamanians were very unhappy and wished to be independent once more.

Thus, when the Colombian Government refused to ratify the agreement which their Minister in Washington had been instructed to sign, American ships were sent to the Caribbean ostensibly to protect American interests. On November 3rd, 1903, a bloodless revolution took place, the Republic of Panama being proclaimed and immediately recognized by the United States Government. Whilst this revolution was being prepared in Washington a new agreement was drawn up between the new Republic and the U.S. Government, in which the former granted to the latter absolute rights over a defence zone as outlined above. The agreement was granted in perpetuity for payment of 10,000,000 dollars cash down in addition to an annual rental of 250,000 dollars throughout the duration of the agreement, beginning nine years from the date of exchange of articles of ratification. This same agreement is in force today, except that the annual rental has been more than doubled!

One amusing incident reported during this revolution is worth recording. All the shares of the Panama Railroad Company were bought by the U.S. Government, together with the other French assets in Panama. When gunboats of the Colombian Navy arrived off Colon, having been sent there to quell the revolution, the senior captain politely asked the American authorities to allow him to transport his armed soldiers and sailors to Panama City by rail. His request was refused with equal courtesy, on the ground that it would be "taking sides in the internal affairs of the country". However, the American Commander courteously offered to permit the Colombian senior staff officers to travel by rail to Panama and thereby help them to "parley with the revolutionary leaders". The Colombian Chiefs of Staff accordingly arrived by train in Panama, where they were at once received by the insurgents and lodged in the most comfortable jail, deprived of their arms. They were released when the Republic of Panama had been firmly established.

As a result of these happenings, the United States was at long last in possession of what is now the Panama Canal Zone and ready to start actual construction of the Canal. The Hay-Bunau-Varilla Treaty was signed, and President Roosevelt appointed the seven-man Isthmian Canal Commission as required by the Spooner Act of 1902. He selected men who were all strong personalities. Admiral John Walker had headed the earlier exploring commission, and was made chairman; General George Davis, a retired Army officer, was appointed Governor of the Canal Zone; and the engineer members were W. B. Parsons, B. H. Harrod, W. H. Burr and Carl Grunsky. It was therefore an Army, Navy and civil commission, with civilians in charge of engineering matters. The grave mistake here was that the principal members were not experienced either in construction technique or in business. They were not capable of handling such vital problems as employment, planning and the necessary equipment for this gigantic project.

The Commission called on President Roosevelt at the White House on March 8th, 1904, and during the interview he stressed the importance of sanitation and hygiene, at the same time warning them that he expected resignations from anyone who found that the work was "too exhausting and engrossing". He ended with the warning, "What this nation will insist upon is that the results be achieved."

The first meeting of the Commission was held at Washington on March 22nd, 1904, and was followed by daily meetings for a time. Their main task was a very thorough search for a chief engineer; a trip to Panama was arranged, and the appointment was discussed on the voyage. It was decided to offer the position to one of the leading railway construction engineers of the day in the United States, John F. Wallace. A letter was written to him on April 4th, 1904, informing him that he was being considered for the post. Accompanied by Colonel Gorgas, the distinguished army doctor who had made a name for himself in Cuba and had been appointed chief sanitary officer for the Canal Zone, the Commission arrived at Colon on April 5th, 1904. They had been preceded by Major William Black and Lieutenant Mark Brooke, army engineers, A. C. Harper, a civil engineer, and Harry Reed, their secretary. There was also Dr. Claude Pierce, the first sanitary officer, who had been studying French methods and Isthmian conditions for some months.

The Commission set up headquarters in a building erected for de Lesseps. At Culebra the Commission found about 500 employees of the New Canal Company at work with a few old French steam excavators, loading dump cars and disposing of the excavated material in nearby dumps. The members of the Commission could see at a glance that recent advances in such machinery had rendered the French equipment completely obsolete.

Although the Spooner Act had visualized a lock type of canal, the Commission examined once more the idea of a sea-level canal, at the same time investigating the summit level and lock data needed for planning a lock canal. After a visit of two weeks, the Commission returned to the United States to organize engineering parties, whilst parallel arrangements were made for sanitation work by Colonel Gorgas and his colleagues. In Paris, final arrangements were made for the purchase of the New Panama Canal Company's Rights by the United States Government. Without the knowledge of Major Black, who was naturally keen to be appointed chief engineer of the new work, Secretary of War Taft had authorized Lieutenant Brooke that he would receive instructions about the transfer of property from the American representative in Paris, and on May 3rd the instructions came. They directed him to receive all Canal properties on the Isthmus from the New Panama Canal Company, except the Panama Railroad, and to be prepared to take over the following day.

Thus it was that a young second lieutenant, only two years

out of West Point Academy, cabled his action to the Commission then sitting at Washington and took charge. He sent a circular to old employees announcing that he had taken possession for the United States and requesting them to continue in their positions. The new organization comprised 746 employees drawing a monthly pay of 15,000 dollars gold; they were organized into various departments, all reporting to the Director-General. Their equipment included 2,148 French buildings, a mass of files and records, and an immense quantity of machinery and rolling-stock. Buildings included the very fine Ancon Hospital, the Administration Building in Panama City, the Taboga Sanatorium, the Dingler residence and the Director-General's residence, used later for many years as the home of the United States Legation in Panama.

At the eighth meeting of the Commission in Washington, John F. Wallace was appointed chief engineer at a salary of 25,000 dollars per annum; he accepted this position on June 1st, 1904, and agreed to maintain a residence on the Isthmus. Captain George Shanton, who had served with Roosevelt as a Rough-Rider in the Spanish American War, was appointed chief of police, a most appropriate appointment! He recruited a force, largely composed of ex-service men, and dressed them in the uniform of the Rough-Riders, which was worn by the Canal police until 1941.

In an Executive Order dated May 9th, 1904, President Roosevelt placed the Canal Commission under the supervision of the American Secretary for War, the reason for this being that the War Department was the Government agency which had charge of civil works on rivers and harbours in the United States. This Order formed the Civil Government of the Canal Zone, authorizing the Commission to legislate for "military, civil and judicial affairs" until the close of the 58th Congress. It vested the Commission with powers to construct a canal, directed that members of the Commission be appointed directors of the Panama Railroad Company, and outlined a Bill of Rights. Major-General

Davis was appointed the first Governor of the Isthmian Canal Zone.

On the day following the issue of the Executive Order, Governor Davis and a party of the first officials set sail for the Isthmus; they arrived on May 27th, 1904, and were greeted by a boarding committee. Two days later the Governor issued a proclamation of occupation for the Canal Zone and appointed the civil officers of the Canal Zone Government. Operation on the construction work was to proceed under the same general system already in effect, but employing American methods of accountability. The one permanent activity of the United States that the Governor found in action was the Quarantine Service. This dated back to 1893, when officers of the Public Health and Marine Hospital Service were detailed to serve in consular offices in Colon and Panama in order to inspect vessels bound for the United States and to sign bills of health.

General Davis worked very hard during his term of service in the Canal Zone, and was certainly the major influence in the formation of the Canal Zone Government. Admiral Walker undertook the heavy task of forming the engineering organization and by the end of May, 1904, engineers were arriving at the Isthmus on every ship from the United States. Yet there was a serious lack of young engineers, who were unwilling to leave the security of the United States for the uncertainties of Panama. Colonel Gorgas, on his return from his visit to the Isthmus, wrote an article on behalf of the Commission entitled "Health Conditions on the Isthmus of Panama", in an effort to counterbalance the harmful rumours which had been circulating about the region. It was his opinion that anyone who slept under a mosquito net, drank boiled water, and slept away from the native carriers of malaria would be reasonably safe. Some American engineering magazines also helped the Commission by publishing articles of a similar nature, pointing out that the Canal would be a "great training school", and praising the chief engineer as being a man under whom it would be "a great fortune to serve".

Wallace had a fine record in his profession. By his own efforts he had risen from the rank of a humble chainman to chief engineer, and one of his greatest achievements had been the transport arrangements for handling the large crowds attending the Chicago World Fair. As chief engineer he had been responsible for the rebuilding of the Illinois Central Railroad, of which he became general manager, and he had been President of the American Society of Civil Engineers, which placed him at the very pinnacle of his profession.

He was a man of strong character, and when he accepted the post of chief engineer of the Panama Canal he emphasized that he could not be expected to take orders in such a large work from each and every member of the Canal Commission, and that he would be unable to give good service unless he were granted an "absolutely free hand". He was determined not to have seven superiors, and accepted the post with that reservation. The greater part of his experience had been in developed country and he had no experience of frontier conditions, where problems of labour, health and supplies were often extremely difficult to solve. However, he felt confident that he would soon gain experience of such conditions. A very ambitious man, he set his sights high.

The most urgent needs facing the new United States administration were sanitation, water supply for both Panama City and Colon, and the provision of an efficient sewage system; many streets of both cities were simply quagmires of filth. As fast as carpenters arrived they were set to work on the repair of old Canal buildings and railway rolling-stock. The private car and locomotive used by de Lesseps for his inspection trips were renovated and used on daily inspections by the officers of the Commission. Ancon was chosen as headquarters for the offices of the civil government. Two old excavators which had been used in Culebra Cut continued at work, but this was the only point where work continued.

Keen interest was shown by the local people when work was resumed, and Sunday excursions became very popular, which was more than could be said for hard work! The needs of a growing population increased rapidly, food becoming scarce and expensive; butter, cheese and milk were at that time unobtainable. Wallace inspected the canal works, remarking at the time that he found jungle and chaos from "one end of the Isthmus to the other", with a great deal of unrest amongst the employees. He even went so far as to state that it would have required from 200 to 300 years to complete the work in the Culebra Cut at the rate of work then proceeding. Jungle had grown around dredgers in the sea-level reaches of the Canal and in the pools of the Culebra Cut, and dredgers were sunk along the canal banks where they had been moored fifteen years before. Jungle had covered railway tracks to such an extent that American engineers continued to uncover sections for many months after the resumption of work.

Wallace gave first priority to Ancon Hospital, where buildings were renovated and staff quarters prepared. Along the line of the Canal, at those places where doctors were stationed, dispensaries were established and converted into line hospitals. At that time the Isthmus was practically roadless, except for old Spanish trails, which had been completely overgrown by tropical vegetation. Houses lacked many conveniences and many had to use candles for lighting.

In his efforts to provide comfortable living-quarters for staff, Wallace started two hotels, one at Corozal and another at Culebra. Unfortunately, he lacked building materials so badly that he was unable to keep his carpenters at work on essential repairs, and had to buy materials in the open market. When his requisitions were sent to Washington, they were considered by the Commission with the usual inevitable delays arising from red tape. But Wallace persevered with his efforts, employing an architect to plan new buildings and repair old ones. He also appointed a sanitary engineer to make plans for the Panama water supply, and these were ready by the middle of August.

At this time there was an insistent demand by the American

press to "make the dirt fly", for the public demanded immediate action. Wallace started experimental excavation in July
with the aim of determining reasonable unit costs, and this
work was carried on for many months with practically insignificant volume. At the same time he placed orders for steam-
shovels, locomotives, unloaders, spreaders and other equipment needed for work on a very large scale.

From the outset, Wallace had to battle against red tape and
Government routine business procedure, which he very aptly
described as "system gone to seed", the tendency being to
consider the way of doing things as more important than the
results. For instance, at one time he wished to advance money
to labour agents. He called in Paymaster Tobey, a man whom
he himself had recommended for this post, and asked for
money. The Commission had appointed Tobey, as chief of
materials and supplies, independent of the chief engineer,
and he had to comply with certain regulations. Wallace
pleaded for urgently needed funds, but Tobey had to ask
embarrassing questions before he could issue them. Wallace
disliked being questioned by a man much younger than himself, and was annoyed by the whole affair.

On August 3rd, 1904, Admiral Walker and the Commis-
sioners arrived for the second visit of the Commission in the
Canal Zone. The same evening, at Ancon, they held the 21st
meeting of the Commission and began a series of sessions
as the Canal Legislature. The flying start of American work
had not produced the results which had been hoped for
locally. For example, Colonal Gorgas had expected to complete sanitation within a period of fourteen months, but both
he and Wallace had to overcome many official obstacles. The
local demand was for greater powers for both the chief engineer and the sanitary officer. Results could not be expected
when they had to depend upon the actions of a Commission
sitting 2,000 miles away!

As the labour force increased by leaps and bounds, rents
and food prices also rose and it became increasingly difficult
for everyone to live within their means. Eating places were

scarce and no effort was made to provide more, but a partial solution was found when an employee died and left a destitute widow. The divisional engineer suggested that she should run a mess, assigned a French building to her, and supplied tables and benches. Soon other messes were established and the feeding crisis was surmounted until the hotels could be completed.

The messes had their troubles, the main one being that there was no cold storage for meat on the Isthmus; all meat was bought fresh from horse-riding pedlars in the streets. There was no ice or fresh milk, all butter was tinned, and local bread was dirty. Fresh vegetables deteriorated so rapidly that employees had to depend largely on tinned foods. Water was another grave problem, and during the dry season it was peddled along the streets, a daily bath being a privilege of the wealthy. In the wet season water presented no problem.

Employees had to find their own quarters. Rooms that in the United States would rent for 5 dollars a month would cost 20 dollars a month in Panama, a rate far too high for a clerk with a monthly salary of only 100 dollars. The greatest complaint was about food, and was closely followed by complaints about the monotonous life, for here was an undeveloped country, with few women and children, and practically no entertainments. Those who wanted to read at night had to use candles or inefficient oil-lamps, which attracted insects through the unscreened windows, and the only course left to the canal builders was to go to bed.

The Canal Commission was extremely conservative in its outlook, reflecting closely the attitude of Admiral Walker, who was an able man but had many set ideas about small matters, and was particularly keen on the need for economy. Colonel Gorgas took requisitions for him to sign, and Admiral Walker would say, "Gorgas, there is one thing certain; whether we build the Canal or not we will leave things fixed so that those fellows up on the hill can't find anything in the shape of graft after us." The Admiral would then place the requisition in his desk and let it rest, and it is

ht, President Roosevelt operates team-shovel at Pedro Miguel in Culebra Cut; *below*, a dramatic ment: the meeting of two steam-vels in the Culebra Cut on y 20th, 1913. The machines in he background are rock-drills

Above, the track is lifted in the Culebra Cut on September 13th, 1913, pre-paratory to letting in the water; *below*, the first nuclear-powered ocean-going cargo ship in the world, the N.S. *Savannah*, passes through the Cut

quite probable that this attitude of mind was largely the cause of the official inertia that gave so much trouble.

When Admiral Walker returned to the United States he was full of optimism for the future of the Canal, but others had very different views. Indeed, Wallace pointed out that it would be some eight months before Panama had its water supply. When he arrived at Washington, he checked on his requisitions and found a most frustrating state of affairs. For example, he had ordered some pipes in August, and the members of the Commission could not agree amongst themselves as to the details of the specifications. But when he said he wanted pipe regardless of specifications, the order was placed with a firm unfamiliar with the expediting of shipments, and the result was that the pipes did not arrive on the site until January, 1905. In the meantime, the trenches for the pipes had caved in because of rain. When Wallace sent cables for checking the filling of requisitions, he was politely told not to cable so much. This kind of pinprick infuriated him.

The Commission was keen for Wallace to return to the Isthmus but he wanted to go on leave. They agreed to this and he went to his home in Illinois. He lectured to the Chicago Press Club on his work, where he congratulated the young engineers and praised the work they were doing. Yet he had no well-defined plans for carrying out the work. He was interested in the scheme for a sea-level canal, for which the Culebra Cut was the key operation.

Congestion increased with the passage of time on the Isthmus, where there were not enough men to unload the ships, and even if there had been, there was a lack of cars to handle rail traffic. Work along the line of the Canal proceeded slowly. In spite of rain, landslides and mud, on November 11th, 1904, the first American steam-shovel started work in the Culebra Cut. At about this time came the first break on the Canal Commission, with the resignation of Commissioner Hecker, who resigned for reasons of health. He was a businessman who had done good work and was

4

strongly in favour of using direct business methods for getting on with the job.

Wallace returned with his wife from the United States in time to prepare for the visit of Secretary of War Taft, who was then preparing for his first visit to the Canal Zone. The Wallaces established themselves in the Casa Dingler, which had previously been the home of the French Director-General, and thereafter their house became the social centre of the Isthmus. Meanwhile, relations with Panama under the rule of Governor Davis had not improved.

Taft was mainly concerned with conferences during his visit and obtained first-hand information of conditions in the Canal Zone. He gained the gratitude of Panama by rapidly presenting what the Republic regarded as a "happy solution" to their problems through an Executive Order, issued by the President on December 3rd, 1904, while Taft was still in the Isthmus. When he left he was given a great send-off, because he had corrected all the "wrongs suffered by this young republic through the misrepresentation of certain treaty rights".

Wallace sent Taft many documents relating to Canal affairs and the relationship between him and Governor Davis. He expressed the view that the Panama Railroad should be in the complete control of the chief engineer of the Canal, and recommended that all its stock should be obtained for the Government either by purchase or condemnation. He also strongly criticized the seven-man Canal Commission, pointing out that it was unable to carry out executive functions from a distance of 2,000 miles. He asked that the Commission should be reduced to only three men—the chief engineer and the Governor on the Isthmus, and the chairman in Washington—all working on purchases, labour and shipping. He thought that the engineers should be consultants, rather than members of the Commission with executive functions. At that time the Commission held meetings to discuss and debate on the most trivial matters, the members holding themselves responsible for each item. It is difficult to understand how anything at all was achieved under such cramping and frustrating conditions.

Secretary Taft began to see the red light, for he referred to the Commission as being "clumsy and ineffective". Governor Davis wrote to Taft that he considered Wallace was "a very superior man, and he ought to be retained". He also suggested combining the offices of Minister to Panama and Governor into one office, which might remove the friction that had developed between him and the United States Minister in Panama.

Work improved in the Culebra Cut early in 1905. The labour force had increased from 500 men in July to 1,200 men in January, two French excavators and two American steam-shovels being at work. Once again the relative merits of a sea-level and a lock canal were discussed, but Wallace would not state his own views in public. He was writing letters to the Secretary for War, highly critical of the Canal Commission, and many letters were written to him by Canal employees critical of conditions in the Zone. They claimed to have been lured to the work by glamorous prospects, but were very disappointed by what they found, particularly those who had to sleep six to a room because accommodation was so scarce.

It was at the beginning of November, 1904, that yellow fever became a subject for discussion amongst the employees, but it was not until the following February that the Panama press became seriously alarmed at conditions in the Zone, when it was reported that everyone was discontented. A few cases of yellow fever were given wide publicity throughout the United States, and these exaggerated reports had the effect of discouraging a large number of men from coming to work on the Canal. Mr. and Mrs. Wallace drove about the streets of Panama City to dispel the rumours, but to no avail; the press continued its campaign.

Wallace later reported that housing conditions had shown marked improvement during his time in the Isthmus, and that in his thirty-five years of experience he had never seen construction men better fed or better housed. He said that the ones who complained were those who had obtained a completely false picture of Panama before they were taken on and that "they expected to swing in a hammock and sip mint juleps and smoke cigarettes and be fanned" all day.

He had great difficulty in obtaining competent men for the work from the United States, and he pointed out that the Civil Service was a hindrance rather than a help. On one occasion he asked for twenty-five track foremen, but when the men arrived he found that not more than two of them could even drive in a rail spike. The only transport experience that one of them had was on pack trains. Thus the remedy was to promote foremen from inefficient men who had not achieved results, but who were retained simply because no other labour was available.

Another of his difficult problems was the Panama Railroad. From the start he knew that the existing rolling-stock and management could never cope with the demands made upon them. With the arrival of steadily increasing freight, the line proved unable to deal with the traffic, severe congestion resulted, and there was nothing to do but obtain complete control. In January, 1905, there were still 1,013 shares of stock outstanding in a total of 70,000 shares, the United States Government having obtained 68,987 shares from the New Panama Canal Company. Acting on Wallace's suggestion, Secretary Taft directed the Company's counsel, Mr. Cromwell, to buy the stock at par plus 5. Cromwell sent circulars to the holders and urged them to take advantage of the offer, but implied that legal proceedings would be taken against them if they did not!

This wily threat did the trick. Late in March Cromwell reported that he had obtained all the stock, and Wallace was told that he had been appointed general superintendent of the Panama Railroad. He would have preferred to be appointed general manager, with the existing superintendent continuing in office because of his long service. The Canal work began to tell on Wallace, who had heard rumours that a man with a salary of 100,000 dollars a year was to be appointed to take charge and to build the Canal. This was not an idle rumour, because President Roosevelt wanted Elihu Root to head the work, and he had even written to Taft signifying his willingness to employ Mr. Root at a salary of 50,000 or even 100,000 dollars a year.

In the preceding January the President had decided that the Canal Commission should be changed, as he regarded the seven-man board as "inelastic and clumsy". On January 13th, 1905, he sent a special message to Congress recommending more power to the President and a reduction of the Commission to five, or preferably three, members. As recommended by the President, the House of Representatives passed a bill embodying the plan, but the Senate turned it down, and Congress adjourned without any action. This failure to act left the Canal Zone without a government, for the authority of the Commission as a legislature under the Act of April 28th, 1904, terminated when the Congress that enacted the law expired on March 4th, 1905.

Thwarted in their plans by the inaction of Congress, Roosevelt and Taft cabled to Governor Davis asking him to continue in the Canal Zone on the same basis as before the failure of Congress to act. Wallace was elated because the suggested reorganization fitted in with his own ideas, and he had attained a great reputation as the first chief engineer of the Panama Canal who had passed through the ordeals of the first Commission without too much trouble. When the plans for reorganization were ready, Secretary Taft forwarded the resignations of the members of the first Commission to the President, with proposals embodying many of Wallace's ideas. He wanted the executive work of the next Commission to be divided into departments, with sanitation retained under the Governor. He also wished the seat of power to be on the Isthmus and the meetings of the Commission to be held there, with an executive committee resident on the Isthmus having power to act for the Commission during its absence.

The President ordered the appointment and duties of the

second Commission in an Executive Order of April 1st, 1905. Shonts, President of the Clover Leaf Railroad, was appointed chairman, and Charles Magoon Governor of the Canal Zone; Wallace was chief engineer and a member of the Commission. The other members were Rear-Admiral Endicott, Brigadier-General Peter Hains, Colonel Oswald Ernst and Benjamin Harrod. The work was divided into three departments, the first being Fiscal Affairs, Purchasing and General Supervision under the chairman in Washington; the second, Government and Sanitation under the Governor; and third, Engineering and Construction under the chief engineer.

All the above men were well known in their respective fields. Magoon had been intimately associated with Taft and had been former Secretary Root's chief adviser on island government; he was also experienced in Canal organization. The second Commission of Construction held its first meeting in Washington on April 3rd, 1905, when the resignations of the retiring Commission were accepted, the work was organized in three departments, and an executive committee was formed, consisting of Shonts, Magoon and Wallace, as laid down in the President's order. In the meantime, Governor Davis remained at his post on the Isthmus.

Shonts had been promised a free hand by Roosevelt in carrying out his policies, yet he found ample grounds for complaint. For example, the requisition clerk in Washington was so overwhelmed with work that some requisitions had not been opened, and some had not been acted upon for four months; others had been divided into parts and spread over the country for political reasons. Wallace had complained forcefully that he could not obtain materials to carry on the work. During the time that the new Commission was holding its meetings, Wallace was on his way north. On arrival at New York he was met at the dock by Cromwell's secretary, who told him that it was necessary for him to be sworn in as a commissioner at once, and escorted him to Cromwell's office.

The reason for such haste was not apparent to Wallace,

who wondered why this could not wait until he reached Washington. Wallace soon found out that the Executive Order had been written with conditions differing from those he had expected. The order provided for a distribution of authority rather than the individual control that he himself wanted. It also required that Shonts should spend some time on the Isthmus. The first meeting between Wallace and the new Commission was at its fifth meeting on April 10th, when he explained conditions on the Isthmus. The following day he was appointed chairman of the Engineering Committee, which was directed to study and determine the best type of canal for submission to the Board of Consulting Engineers, as required by the Order.

Unfortunately, the Committee failed from the outset to work smoothly, because the members who were not on the Executive Committee disliked their subordinate role. For example, their salary was 7,500 dollars, as compared with the Governor's 17,500 dollars and the chief engineer's 25,000; the chairman received 30,000 dollars. Although they did not expect to perform any of the executive work, they certainly did not expect to serve in subordinate jobs, and wrote to Taft demanding a clarification of their status.

Taft replied that the President wanted construction to be placed under the chief engineer and that they were not subordinated to the chief engineer in any respect. Copies of his letter were sent to Wallace and Shonts. Meanwhile the Executive Committee, composed of Shonts, Magoon and Wallace, held its first meeting on April 21st in Washington; good results were achieved for the simple reason that key positions were held by experienced businessmen, resulting in quick decisions and correspondingly rapid action.

Wallace had never liked his appointment as superintendent of the Panama Railroad, and he continued to complain about this forcefully. He was in no way appeased, however, until he had been elected vice-president and general manager in charge on the Isthmus of all affairs of the Railroad and its connecting steamship lines. When reorganization had been completed, it appeared on the surface to be adequate, since a thoroughly experienced businessman was in control. The Governor of the Canal Zone was in close contact with the War Department and well known to the leaders of the United States Government. Wallace at this time was acclaimed man of the hour by the press; the man to whom everyone looked as the builder of the Panama Canal.

In contrast to this lively optimism, Secretary Taft received alarming reports of health conditions on the Isthmus and of the ravages of yellow fever. He implored Wallace to return immediately, but Wallace took a fortnight's leave to visit his home in Chicago. Governor Davis continued at his post, awaiting the arrival of the new governor, and he too wrote to Wallace urging his return. He pointed out that his absence was to be deplored, because at this time the Canal was passing through a transition period. The letter from Davis read: "The old Commission is discredited and dismissed, and not one of the new Commission has yet arrived, while you have been absent for reasons you could not control. . . . There is no head here to command the necessary confidence and respect, and there is a great deal of bickering and fault-finding and scolding among the employees all along the line."

Tents had been pitched for the men working in the Culebra Cut, for the yellow fever panic was just starting, yet in spite of every effort there was demoralization over the whole length of the construction works. The acting chief engineer proved to be unequal to the task of restoring confidence; worn out by a year of hard work, Governor Davis was taken ill with malaria and ordered home to the United States by his doctors. Colonel Gorgas, as Acting Governor, relieved General Davis and continued the struggle to defeat pessimism and prevent the spread of panic, pending the inauguration of Governor Magoon. But the wave of hysteria continued unchecked.

Before he left Washington for the Isthmus, Wallace had a final meeting with the Secretary of War, during which he expressed his gratitude both to him and the President for the reorganization of April 1st. As he departed he told Taft he could return to the Isthmus "with happiness in his heart and with confidence that the canal would be built and that he would build it", and asked him to convey this message to the President. Wallace also saw Shonts, who said that the President had given him absolute power as chairman of the new Commission, which Wallace took to mean that Shonts was going to run the job.

He was entertained in New York by Cromwell, who infuriated Wallace by implying that he intended to interfere with the prerogative of the chief engineer. On the return journey to Panama Wallace was accompanied by Governor Magoon, and while awaiting departure Magoon received letters from Taft expressing appreciation of his seven years of work in the War Department, and referring to a flattering report by the Attorney-General, who considered that Magoon knew more law governing relations between the United States and its dependencies than any other lawyer in the country. Taft also sent Magoon a farewell telegram, which stressed the vital importance of the work. It read: "Make it your first duty. Remember, we stand behind you and our thoughts are always with you; the country and the President have the utmost confidence in your ability to work out problems before you."

There was little formality about the arrival of this pair at Panama. A small crowd gathered around the Civil Administration Building at Ancon on May 25th, President Amador and his cabinet being there to witness the inauguration of the new Governor. Wallace cabled to Taft, telling him of the enthusiastic reception accorded to the new Governor. On the day that Wallace arrived in the Isthmus, Shonts started a speaking campaign in the United States, beginning at the Bankers' Club of Chicago. He outlined the work in progress for maintaining better health conditions and expressed his faith that Wallace would be able to solve the twin problems of excavating the Culebra Cut and controlling the flow of the Chagres.

4*

Wallace worked hard at the new organization, but there were differences of opinion amongst his assistants. They considered that preparation was of the utmost importance and that the output of excavated material was a matter of only secondary significance. Wallace pressed on with actual construction, and would not listen to any change of policy; he wanted both preparation and construction to proceed at the same time, but this was impossible under the prevailing conditions.

The rainy season had started, causing delay, and although sanitation continued, the number of fever cases continued to rise. At this critical stage of the works, Wallace decided to act on a problem that had been oppressing him during his trip to Panama, and on June 4th he sent a vague letter to Taft in which he wrote that "certain complications" in his personal affairs had made it necessary for him to return to the United States upon receipt of a telegram. Yet he did not wait for the Secretary to receive the letter, and followed it the next day with a cable to the effect that "important complicated business matters", which could not be handled by correspondence and which might affect his position as chief engineer, required his immediate return to the United States. He made the curious request to the Secretary that he would order his return for consultation "to prevent apprehension on part of employees".

Taft was greatly alarmed, and conferred both with the President and with Shonts. He was naturally puzzled why Wallace should want to return so soon after having resumed his work, particularly in view of the fact that all his suggestions had been adopted in the reorganization and his power greatly increased. Instead of ordering him back, Taft cabled his approval to Wallace "without knowledge of circumstances that justify". Wallace then confided to Magoon, who at once cabled the Secretary of War, following with letters explaining that Wallace had been offered a position with an annual salary of between 50,000 and 60,000 dollars; that he considered himself essential to the Canal and was at the same time trying to obtain a higher salary. Wallace later explained that he wanted to leave at the time, but did not wish to resign until he had discussed the matter with Taft. He added that his personal relations with Shonts and Cromwell were close to breaking point and that Shonts wished to dominate the work of building the Canal.

All this time, Wallace worked at high pressure on his reorganization of the Department of Construction and Engineering. He introduced an eight-hour day, with working hours from 7 to 11 a.m. and 1 to 5 p.m. At the sixteenth meeting of the Executive Committee of the Commission on June 14th to 16th, 1905, attended by Wallace and Magoon, the new organization was outlined. It divided the Canal into construction divisions, following the French system. When the Committee adjourned, there were to be no more meetings until August.

When Taft received the strange message from Wallace he went to New York to meet him, and Shonts went also. Wallace arrived at New York on June 22nd, 1905, but hardly had he reached his hotel when Cromwell called to explain that he had been asked by Taft to find out the reasons for his return and to discuss them. Wallace refused to do this with the lawyer, insisting upon having an interview with Taft in strict privacy. It was not until Sunday the 25th that Cromwell arranged the interview at the Taft apartment in the Manhattan. Wallace and his son were ushered into the apartment; the son withdrew, expecting that Cromwell would do the same, but Taft motioned him to stay, saying, "I want you to hear all this." Then, turning to the chief engineer, Taft said, "Now, Wallace, go ahead and tell what you came up for." Wallace was irritated by this unusual procedure, but did not protest against the presence of the lawyer. He told the Secretary that he had two matters to discuss, one personal and the other general; the former was his office as chief engineer, the latter the state of the work on the Canal. He explained that he wanted to resign in order to accept a new position that had been offered to him. He explained that he

felt apprehensive about living in the Canal Zone and that he
found life there "lonely and accompanied with risk" both to
himself and his wife. When he had finished this first part of
his interview, Taft said, "Now, go ahead and tell us the
general matters that you want to talk about."

During this explanation, Wallace was cross-examined by
Cromwell, who wanted direct answers to questions about
certain work that could proceed regardless of whether the
Canal was to be of sea-level or lock type. Taft did not agree
with some of Wallace's statements, and Wallace felt he was
being goaded into losing his temper, which he made great
efforts to control. He said he was willing to remain with the
Commission as adviser and help in the preparation of reports.
Taft spurned the offer, stating that he did not want these
reports, and even went so far as to say that he had no use
for Wallace or for any of his "counsel or advice". Taft
bluntly explained that he wanted a construction engineer to
build the Canal and nothing else, and told Wallace that here
was a post to which great fame would be attached. He added,
with brutal frankness, "For mere lucre you change your
position overnight without thought of the embarrassing position in which you place your government."

There was heated argument between the two men, Taft
taking the position that Wallace could not resign and Wallace
refusing to be ordered about either by the President or by
him. Although he was now at a distinct disadvantage, Wallace
said, "You and Mr. Cromwell are supposed to be the two
smartest, shrewdest lawyers in the United States, and do you
mean to sit there and tell me that there can be an implied
contract that would bind me to give my service to the United
States Government forever, regardless of changed conditions . . . ?" To which Taft replied that he expected at least
a year's notice.

Finally, Wallace explained that he did not wish to return
to the Isthmus at all, and Taft remarked, "If you are going
to resign at all you might as well resign now." This was
agreed upon there and then. Although Wallace thought at

the time that there might be reconsideration after tempers had cooled, Taft and the President had very different ideas.

Wallace tried to ease this unpleasant situation, and the next day he wrote a confidential note to Shonts, explaining the nature of the offer he had received, which his family and friends were advising him to accept, but that he felt obliged to discuss the matter with Mr. Taft before resigning. He also stated he had heard rumours that the interview was going to be published, which he regarded as deplorable. He wrote his resignation to the President on June 26th, 1905, and it was accepted on June 28th, with immediate effect. Taft returned to Washington, where he prepared a detailed statement with the help of Cromwell and Shonts, explaining Wallace's relations with the Commission and the events that led up to his resignation.

Wallace was hurt by the statement, regarding it as an "unjust denunciation", but Taft was not thinking about justice at the time, but rather that he had castigated Wallace in order to discourage other engineers from leaving their posts at a moment of crisis. He later explained that he thought he had been justified in his action. Yet Wallace had certainly accomplished something constructive during his short term of office. He had continued those investigations he had found under way when he arrived, started to repair old buildings and construct new ones, initiated work on sewerage and water supply schemes, and requisitioned steam-shovels and other important construction equipment. At the same time, he had in fact delayed work by reviving the now dormant interest in a sea-level canal. After his resignation he suffered severely from what can only be regarded as the most grossly unfair treatment.

He had few friends after his fall from power, and it is comforting to know that the man who supported him most strongly was John F. Stevens, his successor, who knew that Wallace was a fine engineer. He also considered that his resignation was fully justified in view of the methods of the first Commission. Stevens commented, "a more strenuous attitude towards his superior officers would have been more efficacious and would have tended toward a more active state of affairs."

In December, 1904, yellow fever broke out in the Canal Zone, and the wife of the chief engineer's private secretary died. This event spread alarm, but though cases continued to develop during the dry season of 1905, they did not reach epidemic proportions. Wallace's return to the United States in connexion with the reorganization of the Commission in April had increased hysteria and contributed towards a wave of panic. This was not lessened by the fact that the Administration Building in Panama became a focus for yellow fever infection. An auditor and an architect both died of the fever, and Governor Davis wrote of the latter that it was like "the ending of many a bright young man I have seen on the battlefield".

Although the Governor took every possible step to allay panic, the epidemic was in full swing; in May there were thirty-three cases of yellow fever and seven deaths. Funeral processions became increasingly frequent, and coffins accumulated so rapidly on railway platforms that they were ordered out of sight. New arrivals were not exactly encouraged by the sight of the daily funeral train to Mount Hope Cemetery, and desertion became so widespread that it was difficult to accomplish any work. Ships returned to the United States with increasing numbers of deserters; five hundred men returned during the months of April, May and June.

It was hardly surprising that new arrivals lacked confidence, and the old hands frightened them with dismal stories of yellow fever. Often men would arrive in the Isthmus, report for work one day, resign the next, and leave by the same ship, explaining that they would return to see the inauguration of the Canal. Wallace's behaviour on his return in May tended to reduce confidence, and when he left in June he was accorded a farewell by a large crowd of lonely employees who had no idea what lay ahead of them.

Sensational reports of conditions were published in the American press, and friends and relatives of those who remained in the Isthmus wrote imploring them to return as soon as possible. They were restrained to some extent by men who had gone through the Spanish-American War in the West Indies and the Philippines, these veterans urging them to stay at their posts until the new chairman and chief engineer arrived.

After Wallace had left the Canal Zone to consult with the Secretary of War, remours were rife concerning the reasons for his departure, because people could not understand why he should leave the work at that critical stage, and at first they refused to believe that he had resigned, simply because they had such confidence in him. They fully expected that he would return with new equipment and full of optimism, and it was his resignation that sparked off the real panic.

The new Governor, Magoon, had arrived on the scene at a critical time, and although in public he spoke optimistically and confidently, he reported to Shonts that he had found a group of North Americans there who were "ill-paid, overworked, ill-housed, ill-fed", and subjected to the hazards of yellow and malarial fever, and other diseases. He went on to say that these men were all engaged in an effort that involved the prestige of the United States and were under conditions bordering on complete demoralization.

Up to the time that Magoon arrived, Colonel Gorgas had made little progress with fumigation in Panama, where the number of cases of yellow fever in June was double those in May, in spite of the most strenuous efforts to reduce them. Magoon told Gorgas that he thought fumigation should be carried out in all houses in Panama, employing Panamanian doctors as inspectors, and offering them a reward of 50 dollars for reporting any new cases of yellow fever. Panama was divided into districts, and every house was fumigated in a well-ordered campaign, all crevices being sealed with paper. So complete was the sanitation that even the holy water in the cathedral was disinfected.

The work was successful. During July, 1905, the number of cases dropped to 42, continuing to drop steadily until the epidemic was over, and the efforts made drew the highest praise from Taft for both Governor Magoon and General Gorgas. From July 1st, 1904, to January 31st, 1906, there were 134 cases of yellow fever, with 34 deaths. Amongst those who were not employed on the Canal during this same period there were 112 cases and 50 deaths, bringing the grand total to 246 cases, with 84 deaths, and the last case was reported on December 11th, 1905. Since the epidemic extended over a period of eighteen months and there were only 34 deaths amongst Canal employees, the situation was really one that deserved to be ignored, especially since losses from malaria were much heavier than from yellow fever.

There was a sensational press campaign throughout the United States as a result of the yellow fever crisis, largely brought about by the rumours circulating amongst men who had deserted the works or incompetents who had been sacked. This agitation revealed the abysmal ignorance of the public concerning the Canal project and the failure to realize the vital importance of preparation for such a gigantic task. The most encouraging words came from Washington, where Taft cabled to Magoon that he was not to be alarmed by the transfer of power, because a good engineer was on the way and Wallace's resignation provided an opportunity for new life and enthusiasm. He summed up the situation with these words, "Shonts and Stevens will soon be with you, and the mountains will move." They did!

5

THE RÉGIME OF JOHN F. STEVENS

WHEN Wallace resigned, he was replaced by John F. Stevens, then in the service of the Philippine Commission as an expert on railway construction. He had been chosen by Taft and Shonts, who had closely examined the professional records of twenty men and had obtained advice from leaders in the transport field.

Only two days after the acceptance of Wallace's resignation, Shonts telegraphed to Stevens that he had been appointed chief engineer of the Canal works at a salary of 30,000 dollars per annum. The post was accepted by Stevens on June 30th, 1905, and was at once approved by the Commission. On the same day Taft, at the suggestion of Shonts, wrote to the Army Chief of Staff and Chief of Engineers, directing that Major G. W. Goethals should be appointed as one of the chief assistant engineers on the work. Taft was convinced that this officer could be "of great use in the construction of the Panama Canal". Stevens did not accept this help, and in the light of what later transpired it is interesting to speculate on what might have happened if these two men had formed a working partnership at that early date in the history of the Canal.

From all accounts, Stevens appears to have been a man of commanding presence and a born leader of men in this kind of work. His professional record was outstanding; without any college training he started his engineering work at the age of 21 in the City Engineer's Office in Minneapolis, and later proceeded to Texas on railway surveys. He worked on the construction of the Denver and Rio Grande and on the Chicago, Milwaukee and Saint Paul Railroads. He gained valuable experience under the famous James J. Hill, and later became an engineer for a contractor on the Canadian Pacific. He was then appointed chief engineer of the Great Northern, which he constructed over the Rockies to the Pacific through Marias Pass, of which he was the discoverer; he later became general manager of that railway. In 1902 he was appointed chief engineer of the Chicago, Rock Island and Pacific Railroad, becoming its vice-president in 1904.

He himself gave some idea of the breadth of his experience when he wrote, "For three years in Mexico I stood the test of chills and fever incident to malaria. I have slept under wet skies on the Western plains—rolled only in a single blanket, and I have experienced the rigours of a far Northern winter under primitive conditions." He began his work with terrific energy and enthusiasm, organizing a corps of engineers for the work in Washington in July. He did this entirely on the basis of fitness, and was given a free hand in his selections by Shonts. He knew about the food situation on the Isthmus, and before leaving Washington he arranged for a contract to be placed with a Chicago firm for fresh meat to be sent via the Panama Railroad steamers at a cost of about 60 per cent of the retail price in Chicago.

He also called on the President before his departure, stating clearly the conditions upon which he accepted the post. He was to be given a free hand in all matters and he agreed to stay on the job until the "success or failure" of the project was determined according to his own judgement. These conditions were accepted by Roosevelt, and he told an amusing story of an American millionaire who said to his recently engaged butler, "I don't know in the least what you are to do, but one thing I *do* know—you get busy and buttle like hell."

Full of optimism, Stevens sailed for the Isthmus accompanied by Shonts and Colonel Ernst, the latter a new member of the Commission. They arrived at Colon on July 25th, soon after the yellow fever epidemic had passed its peak, with sixty-two cases in June, but there was no special welcome for the party on arrival. In fact, throughout the length of the work there was a state of alarm, and in the same ship that carried Shonts and Stevens to Panama, more employees were booked for return to the United States than had been brought to the Isthmus. Stevens saw all too clearly that quick action was vital. After dinner that evening Shonts called a meeting at the Governor's residence, and such questions as the price of food and recent pay rises were discussed. Some of the men had been gathering bananas in the swamps because they were unable to live on their pay, and eggs were selling for the exceptionally high price of 1.50 dollars a dozen. Even fish prices had risen, simply because the fishermen refused to make two catches a week. They had found that with the large number of arrivals they could make as much from one catch as from two.

Unfortunately, the sanitation campaign was not progressing as well as it should at that time, and yellow fever cases continued at such a rate that people began to discredit the idea that disease was being spread by mosquitoes. The most urgent need, however, was for housing and feeding the employees, involving immense problems of sanitation, markets and entertainments, of obtaining adequate supplies to maintain the working force in contentment and good health, and of forming a strong organization to gather and increase all available forces.

Stevens at once set out to become familiar with the work, and the first thing he noticed was that although supplies were arriving in great quantities, nobody seemed to know where to put them. A large force of men was at work fighting mosquitoes and cutting grass, and both organization and results were lacking owing to such factors as change of officials, yellow fever, and false rumours. The work in progress at that time was of little value to the Canal, and Stevens said of the situation, "in the diseased imagination of the disjointed forces of white employees, hovered the angel of death in the shape of yellow fever."

Getting down to actual construction work, he sought a

way of working in the Culebra Cut, but could find neither tracks to transport the excavated material nor dumps for its disposal. Such dumps as did exist were unsuitably located, and locomotives had to pull loaded trains uphill to dumps that were too high, and which were particularly inconvenient in the rainy season. There was a complete absence of any plan for this work, carried out in a haphazard manner over tracks that were in very poor condition. The French equipment in use was hopelessly inadequate for this enormous task, and only eleven steam-shovels, ordered by Wallace, were working, but they were too large for the small French dump cars to serve. Shortly after Stevens arrived, he viewed Culebra Cut from a high point and saw that seven work trains were derailed and every steam-shovel was idle. The workers were fully occupied in trying to get the trains back on the rails. Seeing at once what was required, he suspended all excavation work in the Cut and reorganized the labour force into track gangs to instal the track system he had planned.

Although at that time the Commission had a few steam-shovels and 60 or 70 large American dump cars of the 300 ordered by Wallace, Stevens discovered that these would not dump sideways, and also that the excavated clay stuck in the rain. Of the 500 flat cars ordered, 250 were in service, not on Canal construction but on hauling supplies. Wallace had ordered only 24 steam locomotives and several types of dump cars, because he had wanted to carry out tests before deciding what type of dump cars he would adopt. Only 350 of the 2,100 French houses had been repaired, because of the long delays in delivery of timber. There was heavy congestion in the docks with insufficient labour for unloading the ships, and Shonts transferred 125 men engaged on the construction of the Governor's palace to this more urgent task.

Within a week important major decisions were made by the Canal Commission. It was decided to double-track the Panama Railroad and obtain new terminal equipment, establish canteens for all employees, build a new hotel as a temporary measure and then construct permanent quarters, placing all available labour on sanitary work, and make thorough preparations for work in the Culebra Cut, using the steam-shovels to maximum effect.

The new chief engineer proved to be a man of brisk action and bright ideas. All excavation having been stopped, there was a labour surplus on the job; men were turned away and told to go back to the United States until they were required. Stevens knew how vital it was on this kind of job to have proper quarters for the men, and therefore regarded the Building Division of the organization to be of primary importance. He gave the fullest possible support to Colonel Gorgas in his fight for proper sanitation, because up to then this valuable and highly experienced officer had been fighting a losing battle with the authorities in Washington.

Stevens realized that the excavation of Culebra Cut hinged on the use of large steam-shovels, such as those used at that time in the mining of iron ore, and fortunately he had many years' experience in the handling and disposal of such excavated material. Building the Canal in jungle country and the construction of railways in the Far West were similar enterprises, and Stevens knew the vital importance of preparing adequately and having suitable plant for such work. He also realized how wasteful the previous work had been, in that money had been thrown away on worn-out and obsolete equipment.

One of the early acts of Shonts and Stevens was to place the Division of Materials and Supplies under a new man. Paymaster Tobey was returned to active duty with the United States Navy and his post given to W. G. Tubby, formerly general storekeeper of the Great Northern, at an annual salary of 9,000 dollars. The greatest problem was to restore morale on the work, and Stevens talked with the men whenever he got an opportunity. His confidence was infectious and the men soon realized that here was a natural leader, instinctively respecting him. With ready wit, Stevens remarked on one occasion, "There are only three diseases on the Isthmus—yellow fever, malaria and cold feet; and the greatest of these is cold feet."

There was no refrigeration service on the Isthmus at that time, and the local resources for storage of meat and food were inadequate. Cold storage equipment was therefore installed on the Panama Railroad steamers, a cold storage plant was built at Colon, and refrigerator cars were obtained for the railway. Soon frozen products were brought from New York and deposited in cold storage at Colon, daily deliveries of perishable food being made at towns across the Isthmus. Feeding some 17,000 men at a distance of 2,000 miles from their home country was a huge problem, for local resources were extremely meagre and the indolent natives had never troubled to plan for the future.

A friend of Mr. Wallace, Jacob E. Markel, who had wide experience in the management of railway canteens, was on the Isthmus when Stevens arrived and was looking for a contract to feed the Canal employees. He had accompanied Stevens across the Isthmus and had also worked out plans for the extension of the Colon food supply depot along the railway by providing small hotels with dining-rooms. Markel had large ideas; he intended to plant gardens near each hotel and grow vegetables, and also import American fishermen in order to establish a local fishing industry. He was confident that he would secure the feeding contract but in the meantime the labour force had to be fed.

Stevens tried to stir up action from Washington by cable, but without success. So he started to operate mess halls along the line of the Canal and he was pleasantly surprised to discover that he could feed American workers for 30 cents a meal. In Washington the scheme for feeding the Canal workers by contract received careful attention, and the Commission called for bids; when these were opened in September, Markel was the lowest bidder at 36 dollars a month. Stevens was told about this, and in the meantime he himself had succeeded in feeding the employees for 27.50 dollars a month, which was most satisfactory so far as they were concerned.

The acceptance of the Markel bid by the Commission created great dissatisfaction amongst the employees. Stevens protested and maintained that this would necessitate an increase in wages, and that there would be "a million dollars clear profit" for the contractor. The contract was therefore cancelled with the consent of Markel, who stated that it would be impossible to do the work with Stevens "cutting his bowels out".

The precedent of the French was followed when it was decided to equip the old Aspinwall House at Taboga as a sanatorium, so that employees recovering from illness could receive the benefits of the island's healthier climate. Additional recreational facilities were provided, and a building was obtained for housing the Cristobal Club. Stevens went over plans for new buildings and recommended a two-storey structure with wide verandas on both floors and space for "billiards, bowling alley, cards, reading and smoking rooms". Club buildings on these general lines were provided at Cristobal, Gorgona, Empire and Culebra.

There was no band on the Isthmus, but many employees were musicians who would welcome an opportunity to play. A plan put forward for a volunteer band resulted in the Isthmian Canal Commission Band being organized in September, 1905, under the directorship of Dr. Sumner Coolidge. Although at first the men liked to play together, before long it became difficult to hold them, and in order to prevent disintegration of this valuable aid to recreation, Stevens reorganized it, with thirty-five paid members and a full-time director and librarian. The Band gave concerts at various towns along the Canal, played at dances and became thoroughly established.

The Hotel Central was at that time the only hotel in Panama City. It was always full to capacity, the food was dreadful, and visitors to Panama made their stay there as short as possible. A hotel at Ancon for employees and guests was considered an absolute necessity, so an architect was instructed to examine the site and prepare plans. Building of the hotel was supposed to start in August, but progress was painfully slow and there was difficulty in obtaining material to meet the architect's specifications, because of the time needed to obtain plaster and metal. Stevens therefore directed that these materials should be omitted in order to accelerate the work. He also inspected all work near Ancon and was infuriated when he found that transport was being delayed by black drivers who gave their friends rides up Ancon Hill.

The Panama Railroad, when it was inherited by the Canal Commission, was hopelessly out of date, and Stevens described it as a "phantom railroad", with light engines and small light cars built thirty-five years before, the only exceptions being a few flat cars and locomotives recently bought by the Commission. Without proper terminal facilities congestion was acute, and freight piled up at Colon, some not being delivered for eighteen months. Cars were delayed for as long as ninety days, and the shipping documents of several cars were lost. Stevens remarked drily that the only good thing he had heard about the line was that "there had been no collisions for some time". He also remarked, "A collision has its good points as well as bad ones—it indicates there is something moving on the railroad."

His first task was to relieve congestion, and he persuaded the steamer lines to take some of the delayed freight, find the owners, and deliver the goods. He also appointed a new manager, and matters improved considerably. The need to ease the congestion was so desperate that old French dump cars were used to haul coal from Colon to Panama, but the small vehicles jumped the tracks. They could travel at a maximum speed of from only 4 to 5 m.p.h. and required about ten hours to cross the Isthmus. Sometimes all passenger trains had to be stopped. The situation became so acute that Stevens said that even if he had "all the steam-shovels in the world, all the money in the world, and all the men in the world", nothing could be done, because there was no plant to haul the material away. Transport was in fact the key to building the Panama Canal.

The Panama Railroad was double-tracked all the way across the Isthmus, except over Culebra Hill and from Mount Hope to Gatun. Stevens increased the dock capacity at both Cristobal and La Boca, replacing the light 56 lb. per yd. rail with the heavier 70 lb. per yd. section. He also strengthened all the bridges, enabling them to take heavier loads. By December, 1905, the congestion had been cleared and the line was nearly rehabilitated; it was to be a most valuable adjunct to the Canal during and after construction. When timber began to arrive, anyone who could work a plane or drive a nail was put on housing work, and by the end of the year about a thousand French houses had been repaired, hotels were being built, and the Canal became a hive of industry.

Stevens began ordering construction plant within a month of his arrival. He placed an order for 120 steam locomotives, 800 flat cars with steam-operated ploughs for unloading excavated material from the flat cars, and installed a compressed air piping system eight miles long in Culebra Cut for working pneumatic rock drills. Shonts was under political pressure to award contracts to particular firms who claimed that their products had been specially designed for the work, but Stevens insisted very rightly on using only equipment that had been tried and tested thoroughly on similar works.

The skeleton engineering organization built up by Wallace was retained for a few weeks, but in August Stevens started work on a new organization. He selected men of proved ability, who in his opinion could "follow general instructions and continue work without constant pressure of an immediate superior". In other words, he expected to be relieved of details and would not tolerate any "passing of the buck". He established the following Divisions: Colon Division, from the Atlantic to Bohio; Chagres Division, from Bohio to Bas

Obispo and also to Alhajuela; Culebra Division, from Bas Obispo to Miraflores; La Boca Division, from Miraflores to the Pacific; and the Mechanical Division at Panama, in charge of all machinery and equipment. There were also Divisions of Municipal Engineering, Building Construction, Meteorology, and River Hydraulics. Competent men were placed in charge of each.

By October Stevens was able to report that he had 60 steam-shovels at work, but he planned on having 100 on the works—80 at work and 20 under repair. At this time he still did not know what type of canal was going to be built, so he worked out three sets of plans in readiness for any decision that might be expected. He estimated that all the necessary plant would be installed by July 1st, 1906. He wisely refused to be rushed into premature work on construction, for in his opinion the French had failed in their efforts because they could not dispose of the excavated material.

The American press noted with satisfaction the improved conditions on the Canal, and one of Stevens's former associates and admirers wrote that only death or breakdown would cause him to leave the work. He added, "Grant him length of days and good health and he will build the Canal— build it honestly and well. He has the soldier instincts of bravery, loyalty and obedience to his superiors. He is rugged as the hills. In all the equipment of experience, aggressiveness, tenacity and mental strength that go to make a great engineer he is qualified for this momentous task." The truth of that admirable pen picture was amply borne out by later events.

The outlook on the Canal was more hopeful than ever before in December, 1905. There were 2,600 men at work in the Culebra Cut; sidings and tracks had been laid; dredging was under way along the Pacific and Atlantic sea-level portions of the Canal; surveys of the Gatun Dam site had started; and the whole transport system for the Culebra Cut was well in hand. The yellow fever epidemic was over, with only three cases in November. Refrigerated food and ice were being delivered along the line, and the families of employees began to arrive by every boat. The President was deeply impressed, and in his Annual Message to Congress on December 5th, 1905, he wrote, "Gratifying progress has been made during the past year, and especially during the past four months." Things were going with a swing.

The Canal was being investigated by Congress in Washington, and Stevens was summoned there, but he would much rather have been left in peace to get on with the job. He could not understand why such interference was being exercised, and expressed his feelings in a letter to the Governor. He wished to get on with the work in a business-like way, and added, "But if I have got to mix and mingle with every politician in the United States, the sooner I will be able to drop it the better I will be satisfied."

In the autumn of 1905 Taft decided to visit the Canal Zone for a second time, and he travelled with a party of officers to Cristobal, where they arrived on November 2nd, crossing to Panama in the latter part of the wet season. Having seen the Isthmus the year before, Taft was impressed by the improvements that were evident. Goethals travelled with the party as special assistant to Taft, who had formed a high opinion of the former's ability. This was Goethals's first introduction to the Canal.

On Thanksgiving Day, November 30th, 1905, the steamer *Trent* arrived at Colon at ten o'clock in the morning. Her passengers included Poultney Bigelow, a well-known American writer of the day, and as it was a holiday, and there was little going on, he crossed the Isthmus that same afternoon, saw the wreck that had been left by the French effort, visited Panama and the Ancon Hospital, and called at the Governor's house, but Magoon was out. In the evening he returned to Colon, where he met two local businessmen who had been disappointed in recent dealings they had had with the Canal Commission. They showed him the sights of Colon, and he departed from Cristobal on the afternoon of December 1st.

The local press announced that Bigelow had taken a keen interest in local conditions, but he was surprised to see that so little had been done to improve what he graphically described as the "Gateway of the Universe". He had wallowed in the mire of the city, visiting about a hundred huts and latrines; he had talked to Negroes, seen the torn-up streets of the city and visited the nearby swamplands. He had been there long enough to write about everything he saw, and did so. On his return to the United States, he submitted an article to *Harper's Weekly* and *Collier's*, but it was rejected. Later he met the editor of a small, reliable magazine called *The Independent*, which published his article on January 4th, 1906, under the title "Our Mismanagement in Panama". In it, Bigelow made a bitter attack on nearly everything he saw in the Isthmus during his brief stay. The article was filled with false statements and implications, but the credulous swallowed it hook, line and sinker, and it caused a national sensation.

Stevens was in Washington at the time, but he was too busy attending Congressional hearings for such nonsense, and ignored the article completely, but Roosevelt insisted on a reply. Stevens, filled with righteous indignation, wrote a scorching memorandum to Taft, tearing Bigelow's article to shreds with characteristic strength and devotion to facts. Taft added further information for the edification of the President, who sent a special message to Congress.

The Senate Committee on Interoceanic Canals called Bigelow before it. He was acutely embarrassed by their questions and replied with hearsay evidence. The members of the Committee tried to make him reveal the names of eminent engineers who, he said, had refused to work on the Canal. At first he refused to answer, but later was grilled by Senator Morgan, to whom he revealed the names of W. B. Parsons and J. R. Freeman. Having given these names, he then wished to withdraw them from the record, but was told by Senator Morgan that he could not swear to a thing and then withdraw it. The Committee could not agree on procedure, the matter was dropped, and Bigelow faded out of the scene.

After attending Committee hearings in Congress, Stevens returned to the Isthmus on February 5th, 1906, where he at once saw that considerable improvements had been achieved in Colon, and observed that his organization was beginning to work smoothly. At Culebra his home was almost finished, built on a site from which he could see the progress of the vital Cut. The increase in excavation began to show a great improvement. In January, 1906, excavation in the Culebra Cut was 120,990 cub. yds. at a unit cost of 72 cents per cub. yd., as compared with a December figure of only 70,630 cub. yds. at a unit cost of 93 cents.

Even at this stage, with the Congress hearings behind him, Stevens still did not know what form of canal was going to be adopted, but excavation at Culebra would clearly count for any plan. Even so, this uncertainty was a terrible handicap to a man accustomed to getting on with a job and finishing it. In March he moved his home to Culebra, which thereafter became his headquarters for the period of construction. In Culebra there were certainly fewer distractions than in Panama City.

Stevens soon made an extremely favourable impression on all those with whom he came in contact. Like all capable men who know their job thoroughly, he was never hurried yet always ahead of his work. He took a keen personal interest in his men, and started the idea of interviews for any who wished to see him about personal matters. Often it was the comparatively minor type of complaint that rankled in this kind of life, and Stevens was a great success at finding acceptable solutions to difficulties. If the occasion demanded it, he could be very forceful, a quality that was revealed when he put down a strike of steam-shovel drivers in 1906 by deporting them to the United States.

He opposed the eight-hour day for work on the Isthmus, because he wanted men to work longer hours in order to finish the Canal quickly. He also advocated the use of

Chinese labour. When asked by a member of the Congress Committee if he thought it would be a good idea for both white and coloured workers to work a ten-hour day, he replied, "I gauge everybody by myself. I work from fourteen to eighteen hours." He was fully aware of the mental change in those under him when they realized that they now had a leader who had taken them through a period of chaotic confusion and who made decisions quickly. He had praised them before the Congress Committee, stating that in his thirty years of experience on such work he had not seen "a more faithful, hard-working, loyal set of men".

In April there were 3,000 men working in the Culebra Cut, driving into the work with seventeen steam-shovels between Bas Obispo and Pedro Miguel, and in June, 1906, the volume of excavation in the Cut amounted to 212,623 cub. yds.; it was during this month that Congress had nearly decided what type of canal would be adopted.

When the Spooner Act had been passed in 1902 by Congress, it was clear that the plan for a lock canal was favoured, based on the recommendations of both the French and American Commissions, further backed up by the long French experience gained on the Isthmus. The sea-level plan favoured by de Lesseps was discredited and on February 1st, 1905, Wallace submitted a report on the work achieved since June 1st, 1904. He estimated that for a sea-level canal the volume of excavation in the Culebra Cut would amount to 186,000,000 cub. yds.; with 100 steam-shovels at work, he considered that he could excavate 30,000,000 cub. yds. a year at a unit cost of 50 cents per cub. yd. Assuming that two years were allowed for preparation, two for contingencies, and six for actual excavation, he predicted that a sea-level canal could be opened for traffic in from ten to twelve years. He also claimed that this would be the most economical type of canal, but neglected to consider the vital importance of the control of the Chagres. He regarded the excavation at Culebra Cut as being the controlling factor. (Fig. 7.)

On February 14th, 1905, the Engineering Committee made

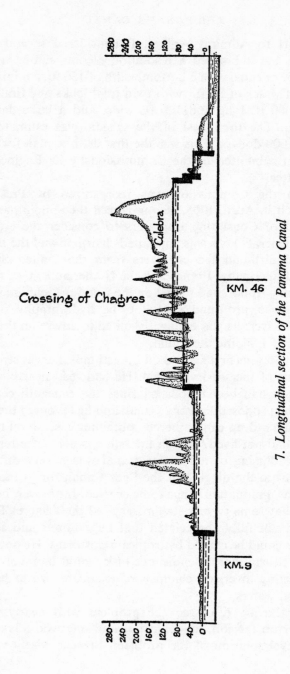

7. Longitudinal section of the Panama Canal

its report to Admiral Walker. It considered several lock projects, but submitted a resolution recommending a sea-level type of canal with a bottom width of 150 ft., a minimum depth of water of 35 ft., with twin tidal locks at Miraflores each 1,000 ft. long and 100 ft. wide, and a large dam at Gamboa. The total cost of the scheme was estimated at 230,500,000 dollars. This was the first definite plan for construction submitted to the Commission by its Engineering Committee.

When the Commission was reorganized by President Roosevelt in April, 1905, he announced the appointment of a Board of Consulting Engineers to consider the type of canal. General Davis was appointed chairman and the Board included distinguished engineers from the United States, England, Germany, France and the Netherlands. One member, Henry Abbot, had served on the Comité Technique, and had made a profound study of the hydrography of the Chagres River; he was eminently suited to advise on the best method of building the Canal.

When Stevens first arrived on the Isthmus, he was strongly in favour of the sea-level canal. He had read nearly everything that had been published since the sixteenth century about the proposed Panama Canal, and he favoured the idea of digging a deep canal, thereby obtaining a sea-level route. But he had not lived long on the Isthmus before he realized that the digging of a Panama Canal was a very different matter from the digging of the Suez Canal, for at Panama there was a mountain range to be crossed. Moreover, he had found that some twenty streams entered the Chagres River, but had not fully appreciated that huge floods and strong currents could be caused by tropical rainstorms. He now saw all too clearly that an enormous task would be involved in constructing diversion channels of adequate size to handle the flood waters.

After having discussed the problem with nearly every engineer on the job, he could not find one who advocated a sea-level solution of the problem. Stevens wisely valued their opinion more highly than that of engineers who had gleaned their knowledge only from textbooks. He therefore inclined towards the idea of a lock canal, recognizing that the key to the problem was the control of the Chagres. The high lake idea would enable the Chagres to form a great lake rather than to be the potential wrecker of the Canal.

Bohio had been accepted for a long time as the best site for a dam on the Atlantic side of the Canal, but Stevens was not in favour of this proposal after his first examination of the site. He had test borings made at Gatun and decided that it was a better site, as a lake formed by a dam at Gatun would handle the problem of the torrential discharge of the Chagres and its tributaries. His idea was that this would make the Chagres the "servant, instead of the master of the situation". From his early days on the Isthmus he championed the idea of a lock canal.

The Consulting Board met at the office of the Canal Commission in Washington on September 1st, 1905, when it completed its organization and assigned tasks to the committees. It then called on President Roosevelt on September 11th, and expressed the hope that a sea-level canal would eventually be constructed. The Board visited the Wachusetts Dam and then sailed for the Isthmus, where they arrived on October 4th, spending a week inspecting Canal works and holding meetings. When Stevens appeared before the Board, he was very tired, having had only five hours' sleep during the preceding sixty hours. He described the French efforts at Culebra as having been nullified because the excavated material could not be disposed of, and compared their earth-moving plant with the modern plant then in use as "baby carriages to automobiles". He said this in admiration of what the French had accomplished with such inadequate equipment.

When asked about working hours on the Canal construction, he replied that he considered 36 hours per week an excellent record for a workman. He appealed for an early decision on the type of canal, saying, "I cannot, and I do

5

not believe any human being can, do much more than mark time until that is done. I can fix my quarters, and as far as my limited intelligence permits me I can contract for certain rolling-stock. I have contracted for two or three million dollars' worth of plant the last month, but beyond that I cannot go."

After the Board had returned to Washington, they continued their meetings, and Wallace testified before them on November 3rd, 1905. He advocated a sea-level canal, and placed some prepared statements before them, receiving a vote of thanks for the "free frank manner" in which he had presented his contribution. He was thereby restoring his damaged reputation. At the meeting on November 18th the members were ready to explain their views and to vote. Mr. Parsons, a sea-level advocate, pointed out that of great enterprises constructed all over the world "there is scarcely a case where the projectors have overshot the mark", and did not regret afterwards their failure to build a large size. He asked whether the Panama Canal would profit by their experience through building a sea-level rather than a lock type of canal.

The vote of the Board was 8 for the sea-level type and 5 for a lock canal, the 5 European members having voted for the former. Of the United States members, 3 voted for a sea-level canal and 5 for a lock canal. The real work of the Board was now over, and it only remained to prepare a majority and minority report, which were submitted to the Commission on January 10th, 1906.

In the United States, a sea-level type of canal received strong popular support, but in Panama the people were more realistic. Stevens went once more to Washington and the report of the Board was placed before him. He supported the minority proposal for an 85-ft. summit-level canal of the lock type as preferable for the safe and rapid passage of ships, and also as offering the best solution to the problem of controlling the flood waters of the Chagres River. He thought that such a canal would cost less for operation, maintenance and fixed charges.

The Isthmian Canal Commission also approved the minority report, but even they were not unanimous. On February 19th, 1906, President Roosevelt forwarded the report to Congress, recommending that a lock canal should be built. He stressed in his message the positive views for such a canal as given by Stevens, ". . . who will be mainly responsible for the success of this mighty engineering feat, and who has therefore a peculiar personal interest in judging aright."

The publication of Poultney Bigelow's article in *The Independent*, to which we have already referred, sparked off a Senate investigation in the form of a resolution on January 9th, 1906, calling for examination of "all matters" relating to the Panama Canal. Two days later the inquiry started before the Committee on Interoceanic Canals, with Taft as the first witness. There was widespread interest in Congress, and a great deal of information was presented to other committees. Mr. Taft opposed any scheme to excavate until the plant was ready, and quoted James Hill as saying that officials would have been "fools to begin any sort of work down there for two years" until the fullest preparation had been carried out.

Stevens was the first key witness, and had ready answers to all the criticism levelled against the Canal. He outlined his plan to build the Gatun Dam with soil and rock from the Culebra Cut, packing the filling with hydraulic pumps. When questioned by Senator Morgan as to the strength of such a dam, Stevens explained that it would be so strong that no power could move it. As for the idea of making it stronger, he went on, "It is like killing a duck; when you kill him he is dead; there is no use in trying to kill him any deader." He also declared that the French Canal alignment had been excellently done and predicted that the lake would form a "body of dead water" that would be safe from currents. He made a very strong case for a lock type of canal, telling the Senators that "for a less price you are getting a superior article". He opposed the construction of a dam at Bohio, because that location would have "percolating material" beneath it and there would be serious loss of water by seepage.

Concluding his statement with a strong plea for a lock canal, he said, "If I had to build that canal with my own money, as between the two plans I should take the high-level plan, even if I expected that my family to come after me for generations would operate it." He made a deep impression on the Committee and was congratulated. Later he remarked, "I have talked a great deal, and I am not a very good talker"; to which one Senator replied, "I am not so sure of that."

If anyone was entitled to talk about this work, Stevens certainly was, for he had made daily trips along the Canal, trudging patiently along narrow valleys and appreciating at close hand the problems involved in its construction. He considered the rock formations in and around the Culebra Cut were very dangerous, and feared that, if a sea-level canal were ever attempted, gigantic slides would occur that would endanger the entire project. In this connexion it is interesting to reflect that a detailed study of the slides in the Panama Canal was one of the early developments in the study of soil mechanics, a comparatively recent science.

Stevens returned to the Isthmus, but he had not been there long before Shonts cabled that he would keep him up to date with developments in Congress, and that he would at once summon him by cable if his presence were required. Stevens did not like this procedure, and wired back, "I have said all I can to the Committee about the type and protest against being called to leave work, as it will be of no benefit." It was not until May 17th, 1906, that the Committee reported to the Senate; it favoured a sea-level canal by the close voting of 6 to 5. Although the Committee battles were over, further skirmishing had to take place on the floor of Congress.

Stevens, who in the meantime had returned to Washington, still pinned his faith on the eventual adoption of a lock canal and was also planning to build the town of Gatun. Because he advocated the adoption of a lock canal with such forceful arguments, he was criticized for wishing to attain glory more quickly with a lock canal than would have been possible with a sea-level canal. But Stevens was not interested in glory, and he stated before the House Committee on June 5th, 1906, "There is a lot of hard work in it; and for any man that goes down there and builds that canal there is nothing left after he gets through."

Even in the last stages of the various views put forward about the best type of canal, Stevens was not dogmatic. He considered that a sea-level canal could be built for 404,000,000 dollars in ten or twelve years, and commented, "I would say to build it that way and drop all other plans; but you cannot do it." He said that equipment would have to be devised for doing this immense job, as it did not exist at that time, and that any lock canal could in due course be converted to a sea-level canal if required.

On June 31st the Senate bill came to a vote and was passed, by the narrow margin of 36 to 31 votes, and was signed by the President on June 29th, 1906. It provided for a high-level lock type of canal with a summit at 85 ft. above sea level, consisting of a large terminal lake on the Atlantic side to be formed by damming the Chagres River at Gatun, a 200-ft. deep cutting through the central mass, and an intermediate level lake on the Pacific side to be known as Lake Sosa. Locks were to be built at Gatun, Pedro Miguel and Sosa Hill. Except for the intermediate-level lake on the Pacific side, the plan was substantially the same as that put forward with so much eloquence and sound technical knowledge by the eminent French engineer Godin de Lépinay at the Paris Congress of 1879, where it was practically laughed out of court.

Stevens and his engineers had worked out several plans in advance, and as soon as the decision had been made they were ready to start the job. Within twenty-four hours the building of the town of Gatun was well under way, and this was soon followed by towns suitable for the Pacific locks. He returned to the Isthmus with Shonts, where he arrived on July 4th, 1906. He was now full of confidence for the future of the Canal, freed at last from the frustration of doubt and delay. Both the sanitary and housing problems had been solved, and supplies were arriving at an unprecedented rate. Refrigerator railway cars were making daily journeys from the cold storage plant at Colon to points along the line of the Canal. There was an effective Mechanical Division in action, with workshops established at Cristobal, Matachin, Empire and Paraiso.

A vast array of equipment had been purchased for excavation and earth moving, including 1,100 flat cars, 120 steam locomotives and 43 steam-shovels, together with unloaders, spreaders and dredgers. The total labour force at work on June 30th, 1906, numbered 19,600. Water had been supplied not only to Colon and Panama, but also to the towns of Empire, Gorgona and Bas Obispo. On the reservoir near Mount Hope the only boat on its waters was called the *Poultney Bigelow* in honour of the great detractor of the Canal. Poetic justice indeed!

The decision to build a high-level canal meant that the Chagres valley would be closed by a dam at Gatun, and that the water would rise over the surrounding country to form a huge lake; it would cover much of the Panama Railroad as well as many towns, transforming mountains into islands. It was necessary to relocate about 42 miles of track, for which purpose survey parties started working at this job from each end of the proposed diversion. In order to avoid crossing the Canal, the track had to be sited entirely on the east side of the Canal. To enable long trains to be hauled across the Isthmus, it was planned to lay the track on the east side of Culebra Cut.

During this stage of the work, the personal relations between Stevens and Magoon, Governor of the Canal Zone, had not been good, and Shonts thought there would be trouble when it became clear that Magoon had been left out of the organization. However, Taft had advised Shonts in May that Magoon was going to the Philippines and that a change would be easy to make.

At this time Shonts wrote a letter to Taft, stating that preparatory work on the Canal was finished and that actual construction was in full swing. For these reasons, he went on, "it would be suicidal to commence the great task before us without a clear-cut organization with centralized power". He asked Taft to request the President to issue the reorganization order so that this would fit in with Magoon's transfer to the Philippines. Stevens also wrote directly to the President, supporting Shonts and stressing the vital need for everything to be subordinated to construction. He wanted to have complete control of the work.

Magoon did not like certain features of the reorganization. He wrote to Taft, asking him not to act until they had conferred, stating that things were moving along smoothly and that he saw no need to make changes until after a conference. Although Taft agreed with much that Shonts and Stevens planned together, he considered there were "some aspects of it that they did not fully appreciate the importance of".

The problem of Magoon was solved earlier than had been expected, for a revolution broke out in Cuba in August, and the United States occupied the island. Magoon's departure was hastened and he left the Isthmus on September 25th, 1906. He was very popular with the local people during his term of office, and received an impressive farewell, with schoolchildren lining the streets, bands playing, and a Marine Guard of Honour. He had achieved excellent results in sanitation and had done very well as the second Governor of the Canal Zone. In recognition of this work, he had been appointed Provisional Governor of Cuba.

Work on the Canal forged ahead. A complete system of tracks had been laid out for the excavation of the Culebra Cut, and plant had been assembled for the excavation on the lock sites at Gatun, Pedro Miguel, and Sosa. The site of the dam at Gatun was cleared, and the necessary tracks were laid for dumping the spoil from the Culebra Cut. Stevens obtained an option on a quarry at Porto Bello and ordered a crushing plant to prepare aggregate for concrete to be used in the construction of the locks on the Atlantic side of the Canal.

Yet in spite of this fine record of achievement on the construction of the Canal, there was a strong undercurrent of criticism in Washington, where it was clear that Taft did not want Stevens and Shonts to dominate relations with Panama. Roosevelt considered that Stevens was an admirable man for the job, but noted that he had failed to train anyone to be his deputy. He also observed that Stevens was trying to be independent of both Congress and Panama as representing public opinion in both countries. His attitude was summed up in a letter he wrote to Taft in August saying that Stevens could "render himself worse than valueless in just one way, and that is by thinking himself indispensable".

Poultney Bigelow's unfortunate article on conditions in Panama had given rise to a wave of adverse propaganda, some of it against various features of the Canal, and some against the actual location adopted. The failure of the first Commission, the chaos that followed immediately after the Wallace affair, and the lowering of morale due to the yellow fever epidemic, all supplied ample ammunition for an army of critics. The President felt that the only way he could answer these critics would be to visit the Isthmus and judge conditions for himself. After much delay, he and his party arrived on the Isthmus on November 15th, and were given a rousing welcome.

The next morning the official party began the trip across the Isthmus, the train proceeding slowly and stopping at small stations so that Roosevelt could see the schoolchildren. When he left the train he was in the forefront of his party and when the train stopped at Cascadas, he greeted a group of natives in Spanish and was acclaimed with suitable courtesies. He then went on to La Boca (now Balboa) where he boarded the tug *Bolivar*, steamed down the Rio Grande to the Bay, around the Naos, Perico and Flamenco Islands, in order to see the approaches to the future Canal as de Lesseps had done many years before.

When the *Bolivar* returned to La Boca after the trip, the President, instead of going to lunch at the Tivoli, suddenly decided to dine with Canal employees at La Boca Hotel, a most democratic decision, which was heartily applauded. He enjoyed his meal, chatted with the men and heard their complaints, and visited the kitchens, where he wanted to know every detail. He then returned to his headquarters at the Tivoli for a short rest.

His visit was of historic significance, for it was the first time that a President of the United States had stepped on foreign soil since the time of Washington. The next day he saw steam-shovels at work in the Culebra Cut, the compressed air drills boring holes in the rock for explosive charges, and the procession of trains to and from the great dumps and embankments. After leaving Culebra he went to Gorgona and made intermediate stops on the way. On his third and final day he was accompanied by a large party of officials, and later he left the Isthmus on board the *Louisiana*, bound for the United States.

During his visit, apart from sightseeing, the President also made certain important decisions, one being his approval of the proposed reorganization draft by Stevens. On his last day on the Isthmus he drafted and signed an Executive Order reorganizing the Canal Commission, and it surpassed even the most sanguine hopes held by Stevens in its tendency towards centralization. It provided for quarterly meetings on the Isthmus and abolished the Executive Committee, organizing the work into departments under the chairman. The title of Governor of the Canal Zone was abolished and his duties were assigned to the general council. Sanitation was separated from government and given the dignity of a new department; the Department of Material and Supplies was placed under the chief engineer, so that in the absence of the chairman from the Zone the chief engineer was to have full power.

5*

All this meant that the centralized organization developed by the French had been forced upon the United States Government, and it was substantially the form of organization which had been recommended by Governor Davis as far back as 1904.

As soon as the preparatory work on the Canal was well under way, the question as to whether the Canal was to be built by contract or by direct labour had to be decided. The French had used the contract method, and Shonts wanted the work done by contract. Stevens had worked with contractors for many years, but he wanted bidding to be based on the capacity and skill of the contractor before he could make a decision. When explaining his needs to Congress in May, 1906, he had urged retention of sanitation and living-quarters under government, but he suggested that the construction work should be let in the form of several contracts, rather than being entrusted to a single firm. He knew only too well that contractors were not familiar with work on the Isthmus and that they were not provided with suitable equipment. He explained that this meant the contractors would have to include all kinds of contingencies in their estimates, thus causing delay in assembling plant and starting work.

Stevens had already ordered plant of the best available type so that it would be ready for the contractors, and he hoped thereby to obtain reasonable bids and save time. Although he backed the idea of carrying out the work by contract, he did not consider that anything would be gained by contract if he were allowed to proceed with a "thoroughly unhampered business administration".

The President was attracted by the idea of rapid construction and also supported the contract idea; in late June he summoned Stevens to the White House and told him that he was very keen to have the Canal under construction by contract by November, 1906. Stevens got busy at once, wrote a strong letter to Shonts, and sent him a memorandum on a plan for the association of ten or fifteen general contractors to carry out the work. He wanted them to have a capital of

25,000,000 dollars and to be able to give a 10,000,000-dollar bond for construction of the Canal. This would include dredging of the sea-level portions; construction of locks, dams and regulating works; excavation for the locks, including excavation of the Culebra Cut; and relocation of the Panama Railroad and the construction of breakwaters. He based his plan on a percentage profit arrangement, with deductions for exceeding an agreed time and bonuses for every month that was saved. He considered that the Commission should retain control of government and sanitation, material and supplies, municipal engineering and water supply, labour and quarters, and the repair of machinery.

Stevens had thought about the contract plan for months. He had used this method on a large scale and was well aware of its many possible pitfalls and risks. His forwarding letter contained a warning note that he was "strongly opposed to endeavouring, by advertisement or otherwise, to let the entire work to any one firm", as that would take too much power from the Commission, facilitate combinations to control prices, and might well cause delays. He stressed to Shonts the absolute need for keeping control in their own hands and under the direction of the Commission's engineers. He went on to warn the chairman that "in justice to ourselves" the work could not be carried out in any other way. Stevens wrote in similar terms to Roosevelt, referring to his letter to Shonts and expressing the hope that the matter would be cleared up by the middle of October.

Shonts was well satisfied with the plan proposed by Stevens, endorsing it as the simplest and most effective method of building the Canal. He promised to submit the plan to both Taft and the President, but asked Stevens to be ready to come north to help in awarding the contracts. By August, Shonts had referred the contract plan to the President and cabled the welcome news to Stevens, "President approves all plans." Although the contract plan was entirely Stevens's idea, the award of the contracts was in other hands.

Whilst the planners in Washington were absorbed in thinking about contracts and contractors, work on the Isthmus
proceeded apace. The volume of excavation steadily increased from July to December, 1906, and the plant was
ready for excavation on a large scale during the next dry
season. One of the last incidents of that fateful year was the
flooding of the Chagres River in December. At Gamboa the
river reached a height of nearly 80 ft. above sea level, about
40 ft. above the bottom planned for the Culebra Cut. This
flood proved that a dike would have to be placed across the
Cut at Gamboa to protect it from the flood waters of the
Chagres and that the old French diversions on each side
would have to be placed in service in order to protect the
Canal works from the turbulent river.

Living conditions for the employees on the Canal had
greatly improved, building construction having increased in
1905 and 1906, reaching its peak of activity in 1907. On
January 17th of that year buildings at Culebra were lit by
electricity for the first time. People no longer had to worry
about the wind blowing out the old-fashioned oil-lamps, and
housewives were relieved from the tedious job of cleaning
and washing lamp chimneys. The streets of Panama City and
Colon had been paved, and both sewerage and water supply
systems had been installed in 1905 and 1906. It was claimed
at the time that Panama was the best paved city in Central
America. About 80 per cent of the excavation and transport
plant for the whole project was either at work or on order,
and dredging was in full swing in both the Atlantic and
Pacific sea-level sections of the Canal. Excavation for the
Pedro Miguel and Gatun locks was well in hand, and by
early 1907 the daily output of all classes of construction was
increasing so rapidly that Stevens felt quite confident of the
outcome. Later he wrote, "The hardest problems were solved,
the Rubicon was crossed, the Canal was being built, and
everything was set for its completion." He gave the opening
date as January 1st, 1915.

Excavation on a large scale began in the Culebra Cut in

January, 1907, when 566,750 cub. yds. were excavated from
the Culebra Division and there was a daily average of 31
steam-shovels at work. The steam-shovel drivers were the
men of the hour, for progress hinged on their output; their
pay was high and was accepted as the standard by which
other groups wished to base their pay. The steam-shovel
drivers felt that their services were more valuable than those
of the steam locomotive drivers, who received slightly higher
pay. They called a meeting and decided to strike for more
pay, appointing a committee to present their demands to
the chief engineer. When the delegation arrived at the office
at Culebra, Stevens greeted them as follows, "Well, fellows,
what do you have on your mind today?" They explained
how hard they worked and how unjust it was that they did
not receive the same pay as the locomotive drivers, their
spokesman announcing that they had decided to strike for
more money than the drivers received. Completely unperturbed, Stevens replied, "Well, you men know my reputation for standing by my men. You all know damn well that
strikes don't get you anywhere. Now, get the hell out of this
office and back to work on those shovels." They returned to
work and did not bother him any more, but went over his
head to the President!

In spite of many difficulties at that time, excavation from
the Culebra Division during February was up again with a
volume of 639,112 cub. yds., and the following month it
soared to 815,270. As the year 1907 opened, the works
showed the fine results of Stevens's campaign against the
inefficiency of the cumbersome Commission. He had developed an excellent centralized organization to replace the
three separate activities of engineering, government and sanitation.

The contract negotiations at this period revealed the completely different views of Shonts and Stevens, the latter being
of the firm opinion that bids for Canal contracts should be
advertised. Shonts, who had far less experience, maintained
that there should be competition on the basis of percentage

alone. He later wrote to Taft, setting forth his reasons for supporting the contract method of construction and recommending that the entire work should be awarded to an association of contractors on a percentage basis, as proposed by Stevens. Stevens was very pleased to learn that his proposals had been adopted, but did not wish to go to Washington as he had already lost much time on his work. He regretted the decision to advertise for bids, predicting that it would become a "conglomeration of bids and powwow that will cause the whole proposition to result in smoke". Shonts assured him by cable that the association would be one of expert firms.

By September the situation had become clearer, but Shonts apparently had to bow before political pressure, for he wrote to Stevens, telling him he thought the plan was ideal and that the President would have supported it but for Taft's wish for advertising. He did not think it would become a "conglomeration of bids", but wanted Stevens to decide on the awards. Under this kind of pressure, Stevens had no other course open to him but to agree, backed by the request that the matter should be accelerated.

Shonts held many conferences with contractors. At first they were antagonistic to the proposals but finally, with only one exception, they agreed that Stevens's plan was the right one. One contractor submitted a proposal that it should be possible to obtain advance annual distribution of the bonus payment. Shonts, instead of rejecting it, passed it on to Stevens, who at once replied that it was "misleading and dangerous". He wrote to Shonts and told him that he knew about contractors from bitter experience, and that when dealing with them "one has to be as wise as a serpent, and apparently as harmless as a dove". Later he wrote that he feared they would get into "endless complications and entanglements".

In spite of the obvious differences between the chairman and the chief engineer, the proposals for bids were advertised on October 9th, 1906, in a form tentatively agreed upon during an informal conference with the Commission. These included directions to the bidders and the form of contract, setting January 12th, 1907, as the date for the opening of all bids received. When the bids were opened, there were only four: George Pierce and Company of Frankfort, Maine, 7·19 per cent; W. J. Oliver and A. M. Bangs of New York City, 6·75 per cent; the MacArthur Gillespie Company of Chicago, 12·50 per cent; and the North American Dredging Company of San Francisco, 28 per cent. Stevens considered that the lowest bid was too high, and wanted to know the "record and capacity" of each firm before he made a decision.

In the midst of all this, Shonts received an offer to head a large transport merger in New York City and decided to resign. In submitting his resignation to the President, he pointed out that it had been agreed he should be released when excavation of the Culebra Cut was under way. Roosevelt accepted the resignation "with extreme reluctance", and in spite of his polite acceptance certain rumours began to circulate. Friends of Shonts said of him that he had become "disgusted with Washington red tape and Washington political interference". Many people claimed that it was due to his relations with Stevens, and it was clear that harmony between them no longer existed.

Shonts's resignation came as a great shock and surprise to the people on the job, after he had received so much praise from the President. The question of his successor was hotly debated and the press was critical, commenting that from the very beginning of construction there had been removals and resignations that became the order of the day. Stevens did not relax, but continued to work hard for his Canal.

The first act of Shonts after receipt of the bids for the contracts was to confer with Roosevelt and Taft, without consulting Stevens as he had promised; they agreed that the contract should be awarded to Oliver and Bangs, the 6·75 per cent bidders. Ten days later it was decided to allow W. J. Oliver ten days in which to qualify with new associates in a corporation backed by 5,000,000 dollars capital, but Bangs was eliminated.

Stevens watched the contract position very closely, and he cabled to Shonts that he thought it would be a grave error to award the contract to Oliver, whom he regarded as lacking in the necessary skill or experience for such a vast project. He strongly objected and pointed out that changing of the associates was the same as allowing a new bid to be made. Indeed, Stevens became thoroughly alarmed about the whole business, for both Taft and Roosevelt were on the point of awarding a contract for the building of the Canal to contractors whom they did not know.

In view of all this, the decision to award the contract to a firm whose capacity he gravely questioned, without consulting him as had been promised, revealed to Stevens the futility of his efforts to protect the interests of the Canal. He eventually decided that only drastic action could save the situation from chaos, which he feared would reach the same state as that of 1905 and endanger the whole future of the Canal. On January 30th he wrote a six-page letter to Roosevelt expressing his desire to leave the Canal and return to his former activities, but for some reason this letter was not received at the White House until February 12th. Meanwhile he continued his efforts to avoid the inevitable abyss towards which politicians were leading the Canal. He confided to his close friends the disgust and irritation which he felt towards Washington officialdom.

When Taft received the cable from Stevens asserting that award of the contract to Oliver would be a mistake, he asked Stevens to amplify his cable with reasons. This was exactly what Stevens himself wanted, and in a confidential cable he stressed that the chief aim of the contract system was to assemble large numbers of the best specialists available for each class of work; he considered that their ability and fitness were far more important than money. Taft again cabled Stevens, giving him the names of other men in the association of contractors, who would have provided a total backing of 1,500,000 dollars. Completely baffled, Stevens replied that he knew nothing of the parties, as in his view they were "not prominent enough to be generally known". He felt that they lacked technical ability for the job, and he refused to change his mind.

The President now intervened and sent a confidential cable to Stevens, naming the associates of Oliver and asking for his comments. Roosevelt added the ominous statement, "I would not be willing now to alter this policy entered into with such deliberation, save for grave reasons which can be stated publicly, and verified." The President was here in a dilemma, for he appealed to Stevens, "I need your assistance in carrying the policy through and I wish full comment from you", both on the bid and on the bidders. This was a strange procedure, to say the least, when, in the early days of the contract negotiations, the points expressed were that the contractors should be of proved ability and capacity and that Stevens should approve the awards!

In Stevens's letter of January 30th to the President, he stated that at first he thought the Canal work would be a purely "business proposition", but instead he had found it necessary to engage in a "continuous battle with enemies in the rear". He went on to claim that he had been continuously under attack by people "I would not wipe my boots on in the United States". He claimed that he had been losing 100,000 dollars a year whilst in the Isthmus and considered that the honour of building the Canal did not appeal to him. He claimed that he could return to positions, some of which "I would prefer to hold, if you will pardon my candour, than the President of the United States". He also alleged that the Commission had not been given a fair trial, but reported that he had a good organization and was confident of a "speedy completion of the Canal". He concluded by asking for Roosevelt's "calm and dispassionate consideration". Nothing was known about this action by Stevens on the Isthmus.

Roosevelt immediately sent this letter to Taft, stating that "Stevens must get out at once". He also indicated that even if Stevens should change his mind, as he had done once before, he would not consider the matter in view of the "tone of the letter". It is clear that the President did not wish to be in conflict with Stevens, handling this crisis on the basis of "meeting his wishes". Taft consulted with General Alexander Mackenzie, Chief of Engineers, who recommended Major Goethals as being the most suitable man for the post of chief engineer of the Canal.

Roosevelt realized that he could not build the Canal with chief engineers leaving every year, and he regarded the Canal as his greatest work, ranking equal with the Louisiana Territory Purchase of 1803. The end of his second term as President was approaching, and the days of preparation and organization were over. He decided, "I propose now to put it in charge of men who will stay on the job till I get tired of having them there, or till I say they may abandon it. I shall turn it over to the army." At the conference the next day Roosevelt and Taft discussed the matter and agreed that a change should be made. The President asked Taft for a recommendation from the Corps of Engineers and Taft urged that Goethals should be appointed chief engineer.

Within 48 hours of receiving Stevens's letter on February 12th, Roosevelt cabled acceptance of his resignation, promising that he would at once send someone to replace him, probably an army engineer. He asked Stevens to continue in his post until after his successor arrived and had a chance to take over the work. He feared that much harm might result from Stevens's early departure and wanted him to "continue without a break".

Six days after receiving Stevens's letter, the President sent for Goethals, who called at the White House the same evening. He was told of the changes which had to be made at Panama, and Roosevelt outlined his plan for reorganizing the Commission by combining the offices of chief engineer and chairman, with the aim of eliminating the friction which had often existed between these two people. He went on to stress that his one objective was to build the Canal quickly, and he was determined to "assume powers which the law did not give but which it did not forbid him to exercise". On the evening of February 18th, 1907, Goethals was appointed chief engineer of the Panama Canal.

George Washington Goethals, who was born at Brooklyn in 1858, had a fine professional career behind him. He studied at West Point Military Academy and was commissioned in the Corps of Engineers in 1880. He commanded a contingent of Engineers in the Spanish-American War, and later worked with General Nelson Miles in the North-west, on the Ohio River, on surveys and on the construction of dams and locks, then served as instructor at West Point in civil and military engineering. He was then appointed engineer in charge of the Tennessee River, which included the Muscle Shoals Canal and the locks, and also served on the Fortification Board at the War College. He was admirably fitted by training and experience for his new post.

At the end of February, Roosevelt wrote to Shonts about the contract situation in an analysis that revealed the strong influence of Stevens, even in the wording. He explained that Stevens, who had devised the form of contract, had advised against the award and that he had received a letter from Stevens asking to be relieved. This removed the chief reason for awarding the contract, as Stevens had been expecting to supervise the work. He recommended that the Commission should reject all the bids received, none of them being a satisfactory fulfilment of the contract. Formal notice to this effect was taken by the Commission on February 27th.

Stevens's resignation provided the President with a way out of his dilemma, and he therefore asked the Commission to appoint Major Goethals chief engineer of the Canal in order to maintain administrative continuity. He claimed that it was intended not to "disturb in any way the present organization on the Isthmus, which is very satisfactory, nor to interfere with the admirable work" then being done by the assistant chief engineer, Ripley, and other heads of departments.

When the news about the rejection of the contract and

the resignation of the chief engineer reached the Isthmus, it was a great shock for everyone, because great results had been expected from Stevens and from the fine organization he had created. In fact the workers in the Culebra Cut were stunned by the news, and the Cut became as "quiet as the grave". One old employee lamented: "Culebra's cut to the heart; we're cut through and through." When interviewed, Stevens refused to talk but stated that the President was entitled by his position to be the first to speak.

The employees felt so strongly about the matter that they started a petition requesting Stevens to remain on the job, and 4,000 men signed. Reed, an Executive Secretary, issued a circular to all the heads of Divisions informing them that this petition was being circulated to show the "loyalty and admiration of the men who have worked almost two years under his direction". Reed was well aware of all that had gone on behind the scenes and that this effort of the employees would be futile, but he was unable to stop the movement. The petition read, "Please withdraw your resignation and remain in charge of our work. We will show our appreciation and loyalty by working for you even harder than we have up to this time." In a few days all the petitions were turned in with more than 10,000 signatures. Some of the men were annoyed by the implication that they had not worked hard enough, for they felt that they could not have worked any harder, and many of them changed the above phraseology in their copies. On that particular aspect, Stevens said some years later, "I didn't loaf very much myself in the old days when I was on the Isthmus—and one regret that I still have is that I didn't work everybody harder."

The men organized a collection for three presents for Stevens that could be passed on to his sons—a gold watch, a diamond ring and a silver table-set, which included a tray bearing an engraving of the completed Canal. So highly was this man esteemed, that everyone wished to contribute. There was widespread consternation at the appointment of an army man to relieve Stevens, for it was feared that regimentation would ensue. They wondered if they would have to salute the boss, and if it would be an advantage to extend their military vocabulary.

The extraordinary thing about all this tragic business was that Stevens never revealed precisely why he resigned, and carried his secret with him to the grave. His only public statement was that the reasons were "private and of no particular interest to the public" and that there had not been the slightest friction between him and the President. However, when an objective view of the whole matter is taken, it seems clear that his removal provided a convenient way out of the contract impasse into which the Administration had drifted, and which had been entirely created by men who were not competent in business, nor familiar with the requirements of civil engineering contracts. He certainly appears as a sacrifice on the altar of political expediency.

One of the first acts of the President in this crisis was to appoint Stevens as chairman by an Executive Order, thus making him both chief engineer and chairman. This was the combination that Roosevelt wanted in order to remove friction, and had been previously recommended by Stevens. It greatly facilitated the transfer of power from Stevens to Goethals. The latter arrived at Cristobal on March 12th, and was warmly greeted by Stevens. When asked by press reporters what changes he intended to make, he replied that none whatever would be made in the "splendid organization" that Stevens had built up, and that the work would continue without interference.

At midnight on Saturday, March 31st, 1907, Stevens terminated his service with the Panama Canal and Goethals took over. His last days on the work to which he had given so much were free of worry and responsibility, but Goethals showed what a great man he was by gaining the full confidence of those around him almost at once. Stevens planned to leave the Isthmus on April 7th, and employees arranged to give him a farewell reception on Pier 11 at Cristobal. Special trains were run for guests from all along the line of the Canal, and the pier was decorated with lights and flags. At 9.30 that evening Stevens appeared with a group of close friends, and it was nearly midnight when he went on board the tug *Gatun*, waiting to take him to the liner *Panama*. To the young captain of the tug he said, with tears in his eyes, "Captain, I am ready." He had been overpowered by the demonstration of affection. At noon the next day he sailed for the United States to the tune of Auld Lang Syne, played by the band he had created.

6

THE ADVENT OF GOETHALS

IT was a great achievement that Goethals became a success-ful follower of Stevens at the peak of his tremendous popularity with the Canal employees. The new chief engineer was confronted with difficulties heavy enough to test the character and ability of any man.

From the very outset, he was full of admiration for the fine organization he had inherited. The transport system was complete, and about 80 per cent of the plant required for the job was on hand. Excavation in the Culebra Cut and hauling of the excavated material to the dumps was proceeding at a cracking pace, and four steam-shovels were at work excavating the site of the Gatun Lock. Dredgers for both the Atlantic and Pacific sea-level sections of the Canal were either at work or being built under contract, and surveying work was almost complete. Large workshops were operating at Gorgona, and others were under construction at Empire and Paraiso. The site for the Gatun Dam had been cleared.

Health conditions were excellent and the Health Department was well organized. There was no yellow fever and only very little malaria, although the total Canal force on June 30th, 1907, numbered 29,446. Goethals was deeply impressed by the work already done, but he realized that a huge task remained to be completed. Taft's first action was to strengthen Goethals' position as chairman, and he signed an Executive Order on April 2nd, 1907, giving effect to this. Goethals found that he was now chairman, chief engineer and Governor of the Canal Zone, but the Commission was still charged with the responsibility for building the Canal and therefore potential trouble lay ahead.

Goethals initiated a system of daily inspections, and after an early breakfast he would walk down the hill to Culebra Station to board a north-bound or south-bound train, or to take his special, yellow-painted inspection car, nicknamed the "yellow peril". He always seemed to turn up on the job at unexpected times, but always returned to his office in the afternoons, where he worked until ten or eleven at night to produce enough instructions to keep the men at work the next day. Although in the beginning he thought the job would be too much for him, he soon gained a sense of perspective and was able to cope with all the irritating details that his job demanded.

The first four clubhouses—at Empire, Culebra, Gorgona and Cristobal—were nearing completion when Stevens left, but he was unable to open them before he left, as he had hoped. The first clubhouse was inaugurated at Gorgona under the auspices of the Y.M.C.A.; it was a two-storey building with wide verandas and a spacious lobby. There were smoking-rooms, a gymnasium, a library of 600 volumes and a soda fountain. All the clubhouses provided centres of community life for the employees and gave them an escape from the boredom and monotony of life in the tropics.

The vital department of sanitation was under the control of another remarkable man, Colonel Gorgas. He was born in Mobile in 1854, where he qualified at the Medical School and was appointed Lieutenant in the United States Army Medical Service in 1880, being promoted Captain in 1885 and Major in 1898. He gained international prestige in his victorious campaign against yellow fever in Cuba from 1898 to 1902. In 1904 he was appointed Director of Medical and Sanitation Services in the Panama Canal Zone, where he served in that capacity until 1913. He was later promoted General and appointed Director-General of Medical Services of the United States Army, a post which he held from 1914 to 1918. On his retirement from active service he joined the International Health Board and initiated a campaign against yellow fever.

The construction of the Panama Canal was not only a triumph of engineering skill, but equally an outstanding victory for medical research and sanitation in conquering the ravages of the mosquito. The French effort was largely nullified by unhealthy conditions on the Isthmus, and subsequent medical research had a widespread influence on the development of tropical lands all over the world.

Malaria and yellow fever were the twin scourges of the Panama Canal works. The word "malaria" is of Italian origin, from *mala*, meaning bad, and *aria*, meaning air. It is also used in Spanish, having been associated with miasmatic swamps. Yellow fever is swift and deadly in action; malaria does its deadly work more slowly. It seems amazing that the French Canal builders do not appear to have taken any effective measures against these diseases, yet in all fairness it should be pointed out that neither the causes nor the remedies were then as scientifically known as they later became through painstaking research. Even so, it is still surprising that so little effort was made by the French doctors on site to improve matters. During the period of the French effort, some 88,000 men were employed, giving an annual average labour force of 10,880; of these, 52,814 were treated for illness and the number of deaths was 5,627, giving an annual average of 703 deaths and 6,535 cases. In September, 1884, the earlier conditions on the Isthmus were revealed by the fact that the entire crew of a British brig died from yellow fever, and there were 120 cases in Colon, with a two-thirds mortality. In that month alone the Canal Company buried 654 of its people.

Yet in spite of these terrible conditions, the French Canal Company spent a mere 2,000,000 dollars on hospital services during their régime, equivalent to half of one per cent of the total expenditure, with practically no allowance for sanitation. However, during the American rule in 1904–5, the "mosquito theory" was derided by people who ought to have known better, and some Canal employees on the site "even tore holes in the wire screens that the Commission had

allowed the sanitary corps to put up". Under the French administration, and even under the Americans in their early
efforts, the value of human lives appears to have taken second
place in relation to the value of property. In early 1904, when
the first American Commission started work on the Canal,
there were no cases of yellow fever or plague on the Isthmus,
but a few cases appeared soon afterwards. In July of that year
American sanitary officers appeared on the scene, and under
an executive order of President Roosevelt the best medical
experts were sent out, but their efforts were seriously ham-
pered by red tape. Yellow fever cases increased and panic
ensued.

It was at this crisis that Colonel Gorgas took charge of the
Department of Sanitation. In his report to the Commission
he stated: "The experience of our predecessors was ample to
convince us that unless we could protect our force against
yellow fever and malaria we would be unable to accomplish
the work." The natives of Panama were immune to yellow
fever, which only attacked foreigners. In April, 1905, amongst
the three hundred non-immune employees of the Commission in the administration building in Panama, there were
nine cases and two deaths; in May there were thirty-three
cases and eight deaths. In June there were nineteen deaths
from yellow fever throughout the Isthmus, and the Commission reported that "a feeling of alarm almost amounting to a panic" spread amongst the Americans on the
Isthmus.

Many Americans resigned and returned home, others became lethargic or fatalistic, convinced that no remedy existed,
and there was even a tendency towards abandoning preventive measures. The gravity of the crisis was all too clear;
deaths from yellow fever for the twelve months from October, 1904, to September, 1905, amounted to thirty-seven in
a total labour force of seventeen thousand. This was low in
relation to the normal population of the Isthmus, including
those at work on the Canal. Amongst the latter, from May to
August, there were forty-seven deaths with one hundred and

eight from malaria. Deaths from malaria generally occurred within a fortnight, but those from yellow fever in from four days to a fortnight, and the average time was about ten days. Decisive and effective action was therefore vital.

The battle against these terrible diseases was fought with scientific thoroughness. By that time it was generally known that both yellow fever and malaria are induced and propagated by mosquitoes of two different types. Careful tests, undertaken all over the world by people of different nationalities, had proved this basic fact. It was revealed that malaria is caused by a parasite and yellow fever by a virus, introduced into the blood by the bites of certain species of mosquitoes, and this discovery was at that time comparatively recent. From the time of Hippocrates, however, malarial fevers had been closely observed, and various theories put forward; although some of these were vague, they did anticipate with surprising accuracy the later results of modern research. It was not until the end of last century that the true nature of these diseases was discovered.

In 1880 the French army surgeon Laveran, working in Algeria, observed the living parasites under the microscope in the blood of a malarial patient. His work was followed by that of Italian pathologists, to whom malaria was of special interest, and they confirmed the findings of Laveran. Yet the origin of the parasite in human blood was still unknown at that time, although there did exist an old popular belief that malaria was connected with mosquitoes.

In 1894 Sir Patrick Manson suggested that the malarial parasite was propagated outside the human body, and that its "host" would probably be one particular type of mosquito. Then Major Ronald Ross, at that time employed in the Indian Civil Service, pursuing the same line of inquiry, discovered between 1895 and 1897 that if a certain genus of mosquito sucked malarial blood, parasites were imbibed, and by studying the malaria of birds he worked out the life cycle of the parasites. He discovered that it was only mosquitoes of the genus *Anopheles* which had parasitic cysts on the outer wall of the stomach. It was a natural step from these discoveries to their application to the malaria of man.

The conclusions reached from a microscopical examination in a laboratory were confirmed by practical tests, carried out both at the Italian School and at the London School of Hygiene and Tropical Medicine; further tests were also undertaken in the Roman Campagna district during a severe malarial season. The observers escaped infection by protecting themselves from the mosquito in a hut of special design, those outside the hut suffering severely from the disease. Mosquitoes caught by the observers were sent to London, where they produced malaria in persons who voluntarily submitted themselves to the bites. Ross joined the Liverpool School of Tropical Medicine in 1898 and further experiments were conducted on a wide scale in the Campagna, with results that confirmed the soundness of the mosquito-parasitic theory of malaria.

This fact proved that the mosquito acts as an intermediary host, transmitting the parasite to human beings, and it explained certain anomalous conditions relating to the occurrence of malaria. This disease was always associated with watery exhalations and the fall of dew, but for a long time it had been noted that the passage of the infection seemed to be prevented by a wall of trees, or by clearing a space in the brushwood surrounding a dwelling, and that the "miasma" of swamps did not act at a certain distance from the ground, but was harmful even on ground at 7,000 ft. or more above sea level, and most particularly in broken ground where stagnant pools of water abounded. This has been largely explained by the fact that the insects cannot rise more than a limited height from the ground owing to their restricted power of flight, so that they are unable to make their way through even a moderately thick belt of trees. Furthermore, they cannot fly more than a certain distance, and if they are to breed successfully over a wide area, a chain of pools or swamps is necessary, separated not further apart than this limited distance.

The anopheles mosquito is widely distributed throughout Europe, Asia, Africa and America. The preventive methods originally employed involved destruction of the breeding-grounds by draining pools and collections of water, or temporarily treating them with petroleum, which effectively prevented the development of the larvae; and by protecting the doors and windows of dwellings with wire gauze.

The main attack nowadays is directed against the *adult* mosquito with the aid of a residual insecticide such as DDT, which has made eradication possible. Modern experience has proved that the anti-larval methods are useless except in specific localities such as Singapore or the Panama Canal Zone. Most suppression today depends upon Chloroquine, Mepacrine and Paludrine. Trouble is being caused by growing resistance to these drugs, but they are still much more widely used and more effective than quinine.

Yellow fever is also transmitted by the mosquito, and the first authentic account of its existence came from Barbados in 1647, when it was described as a "nova pestis" and was connected with the arrival of ships. This fever raged at various times in West Indian ports, as well as in those of the American Continent until recent times. During the great yellow fever period, from 1793 to 1805, the disease appeared at various Spanish ports, causing thousands of deaths. It even spread as far north as Quebec, but in Africa it was known only on the west coast. Mortality from this disease is generally very high and in Rio de Janeiro in 1898 it reached more than 94 per cent.

Yellow fever was at first ascribed to almost the same causes as malaria, but as early as 1881 Dr. Charles Finlay produced a theory that the real carriers of infection were mosquitoes, a theory which remained neglected until the part played by these insects in other tropical diseases aroused fresh interest. Finlay revealed that *Stegomyia fascinata* (now called *Aedes aegypti*), a large grey culicine mosquito with silvery markings on the thorax, was the agent; generally found breeding in stagnant water near dwelling-places. Tests were made by

Walter Reed, in which mosquitoes were caught and fed upon yellow-fever patients. After being kept for a fortnight, they were "allowed to bite susceptible individuals, who, for the purpose were established in a camp, with other susceptible persons as a control". Those bitten developed the fever, but others did not. These tests were followed by the appointment of an American commission, the members of which found that the mosquitoes fed on yellow-fever blood were not capable of causing infection until a period of twelve or fourteen days had elapsed, but the insects retained their power as long as they lived. This period was long enough to spread the disease by a ship voyaging to any part of the world.

It was found that yellow fever requires "an alternate passage through a vertebrate and an insect host". The members of the French yellow-fever commission to Rio de Janeiro discovered the curious fact that, in the case of the genus *Stegomyia*, the female, before laying her eggs, must have a feed of blood, and at that period she strikes both by night and by day. Her eggs are laid three days after this feast of blood, and then she strikes only at night. Knowing these facts, American doctors undertook a vigorous campaign to fight yellow fever in Havana, Cuba, in 1901 during the American occupation and cleansing of that city after the Spanish-American war. This work was under the direction of Major W. C. Gorgas, later appointed to Panama, where he did such valuable work. Some Cubans strenuously opposed his efforts on the grounds that he was intruding upon their domestic life, which detailed inspection clearly involved. Strict orders were issued that every receptacle containing water had to be kept mosquito-proof, and sanitary inspectors maintained a house-to-house visiting round. All receptacles found to contain larvae were destroyed, fines were inflicted if necessary, puddles and possible breeding-grounds were treated with petroleum or eliminated by drainage. Hospitals and houses in which there were yellow-fever patients were screened with protective wire gauze, and buildings and out-houses were fumigated with pyrethrum powder.

At first the Cubans looked upon these precautions with contempt, evading them wherever possible. Havana, a tideless seaport, was at that time very dirty, yet the results achieved exceeded all expectations, and after January, 1902, yellow fever was no longer transmitted in Havana. Similar results followed in other places where the same procedure was followed. In Rio de Janeiro, for example, where there had been 28,078 deaths from yellow fever in thirteen years, the disease largely disappeared in 1909; the methods were equally successful in the West Indies and in New Orleans.

These methods for combating both malaria and yellow fever were successfully employed by Colonel Gorgas in the Panama Canal Zone. In April, 1905, the total complement of the Sanitation Department under this officer amounted to 4,100 men, engaged only on matters connected with the extermination of mosquitoes. All fever cases were taken to buildings carefully screened by wire gauze or, if they remained in their own homes, the doors and windows were screened in a similar manner. Copper gauze of fine mesh was used, because nothing else would successfully resist the corrosive attack of a tropical atmosphere. The purpose of thus enclosing the patients was to prevent infection of healthy insects, thereby effectively preventing the spread of the disease. All dwellings in Panama and Colon were fumigated with pyrethrum powder or with sulphur, and cleared of dust and refuse.

As in the case of Cuba, local opposition by the natives was considerable, because they themselves were immune from the disease. Panama, at the time when the Americans took over the work of canal building, was a picturesque and dirty town, and along its narrow streets ran gutters choked with refuse, after the manner common in the district. One of the first jobs undertaken by the Americans was the provision of a good water supply from a reservoir, and mains instead of the tanks, cisterns, tubs and even jars previously employed for domestic water supplies. Ruts and holes in the streets and alleys of Panama and Colon were filled in and pavements were provided.

In order that maximum destruction should be inflicted on the malaria mosquitoes, pools and swamps were drained wherever possible, or alternatively they were oiled. Although the anopheles is a mosquito found mainly in country districts, Panama, Colon and some forty or more towns and villages along the line of the Canal were all exposed to the disease. Full advantage was taken of the fact that the maximum flight of these insects is about 200 yds., and therefore all breeding-places within this radius were destroyed. It was clearly impossible to do this in every case, and reliance was therefore placed on the efficient screening of buildings.

The methods used for the destruction of the breeding-places of the anopheles involved the cutting down of jungle and brushwood with a machete, the large knife used for such work all over Latin America, wielded with telling effect by expert foresters. Streams and ditches were cleaned by pouring oil in them, and the holes of all vermin and land-crabs were stopped. Drainage of the subsoil was carried out with agricultural drains, this being the only effective permanent method of making the soil unfit for breeding mosquitoes. Iron cans were placed on planks spanning the heads of streams and rivulets, and from an overhanging length of wick oil dropped and spread over the water; to the oil were added crude carbolic acid, resin and caustic soda.

The first European workers who arrived on the job were quartered in unscreened buildings, and they suffered to the extent of 33 per cent of their number being attacked by malaria. But only 4 per cent of the second shipload, housed in screened buildings, were attacked. During 1906, when 26,000 men were at work on the Canal, there were 21,740 cases of malaria admitted to the hospitals. Mortality from this disease was two per thousand amongst the Whites and eight per thousand amongst the Negroes. In 1907, with 39,000 men at work, there were 16,750 cases, and the Negro mortality fell to four per thousand. The total mortality from all causes, including malaria, during that year was given as 16·7 per thousand for White workers and 33·3 per thousand

Above, two of the parallel locks at Gatun in November, 1913; *below*, a ship passing through Gatun lock. Several of the electric towing vehicles, known as "Mules", can also be seen

Above, the opening of Gatun lock; *below,* a ship passing through one of the present Canal locks with inches to spare amply illustrates the need for a new waterway

for coloured, amounting to 28·8 per thousand for the total, but many of the cases were due to accidents.

Of the American women and children in Commission quarters at that time there were 1,337 cases, with nine deaths, representing an average annual mortality of 6·73 per thousand. In 1908 the mortality amongst the average number of white workers employed was 15·34 per thousand, and amongst the 5,000 American employees the figure was 8·14 per thousand. Amongst the coloured workers, averaging 31,000, the mortality was 19·48 per thousand, less than that of New York City at the time. In the following year, 1909, conditions improved still further. Total admissions to hospitals and sick-camps amounted to 46,194, or 23·49 per thousand of the labour force on the payroll, but the majority were trivial cases. The total number of deaths was 530, equal to the very low mortality of 11·97 per thousand.

The striking improvement was partly due to better feeding. Amongst the 40,000 employees during the year ending June, 1912, there were 7,000 cases of malaria in the hospitals, with thirty-two deaths, of whom twenty-two were white people; this provides a sharp contrast with the appalling figure of 21,740 cases in 1906. Amongst the "screened" Americans the mortality was reduced to only 3·94 per thousand. It was estimated that the total cost of the Sanitary Department was 20,000,000 dollars, about 5 per cent of the total cost of the Canal.

It should be emphasized that one difficulty of completely stamping out malaria rests in the fact that a malarious person can remain infective to the anopheles for about three years, in contrast with the three days of yellow fever. Workers on the Isthmus also suffered from pneumonia, more particularly the coloured labourers, the disease resulting generally from a low living standard. The fact remains that the excellent results achieved on this great work influenced medical practice and preventive methods throughout the world.

Before de Lesseps was compelled to abandon his attempt to build the Panama Canal, he had lost by disease 6·4 per

6

cent of his labour force and 7·2 per cent of the European
personnel on his staff. As a result of Gorgas' work as
Director of Sanitation of the Panama Canal Zone, the mortality in 1905 was 66 per 1,000, which was reduced to only
21 per 1,000 by 1915; these figures apparently covered all
identified diseases. It would be no exaggeration to claim
that Gorgas' work paved the way for Goethals' triumph in
his accomplishment of that great engineering feat.

Goethals closely examined the organization that he took
over. As desired by the President, the members of the new
Commission were required to live on the Isthmus and to
work as heads of departments. Sibert was placed in charge
of Lock and Dam Construction; Gaillard of Excavation and
Dredging; Rousseau was responsible for Municipal Engineering, Motive Power and Machinery, as well as Building Construction; Colonel Gorgas was Chief Sanitary Officer; and
Jackson Smith was placed in charge of Labour, Quarters
and Subsistence. Joseph Ripley, who had worked under
Stevens as assistant chief engineer and been in charge of Lock
and Dam Construction, was appointed to the post of design-
ing engineer. Major H. F. Hodges was appointed general
purchasing officer, in charge of the Washington office. The
organization of the construction divisions remained the same
as it had been under Stevens.

It was natural that there should have been some apprehension on the part of the civilian officers when they were
placed under an army engineer, but this gradually vanished
as the men became familiar with the new leaders and were
able to appreciate their sterling qualities. Mr. Ripley, however, was not satisfied with the new arrangement and resigned
in protest. The new Commission now got into its stride as a
permanent body.

Mr. Taft returned to Washington, where he took up the
demands of the steam-shovel drivers who, it will be remembered, had written to the President after their demand for
increased pay had been turned down by Stevens. Both he
and the President were prepared for trouble, but they also

knew only too well that the shovel drivers had no real grievance, because in any case they were the highest-paid group on the construction work. The Government could not afford to yield to their demands under pressure for an increase from 210 dollars to 300 dollars per month, which at that time would have established a costly precedent. On Sunday, May 5th, 1907, Taft published his decision that he wanted both the locomotive and the steam-shovel drivers to receive the same pay. He authorized an increase to transport crews and seniority of 5 per cent for the first year, with 3 per cent for each succeeding year to steam-shovel, transport and mechanical trades employees.

This was a compromise, and like so many compromises it did not work. The steam-shovel men went on strike, and overnight the number of steam-shovels at work was reduced from 68 to 13. Many strikers left for the United States, and the excavation in the Culebra Cut fell to a low record of 624,586 cub. yds. in June, a severe setback to the works. Goethals recruited fresh crews, and the volume of excavation increased slowly but surely as they gained experience. Many of the strikers returned later, only to find that they had lost their seniority, which was dependent on continuous service. They had to start all over again. It was not exactly a victory for Goethals but it taught him how to deal with strikers.

This crisis having been surmounted, the next problem to be solved was the much-discussed contract matter, a legacy from the Stevens régime. Contractors had continued to exert pressure on Taft in Washington, but Goethals wisely referred the problem to the Engineering Committee composed of Gaillard, Sibert and Rousseau. They reported adversely, which fortified Goethals in his official position. He wrote to Taft explaining how the work divided itself naturally into dry excavation by steam-shovels in the Culebra Cut; excavation by dredgers in the sea-level portions of the Canal; the construction of locks, dams, regulating works and terminals; and the relocation of the railway track.

Until September, 1907, the Canal Commission had published

no regular bulletin of information, and workers had complained about this to Miss Beeks, a social worker who had been visiting the Canal. She mentioned the subject to Colonel Goethals, and he at once engaged a young editor to start the *Canal Record*, a weekly newspaper issued free to all employees. It gave accurate information and thereby stopped many false rumours from circulating, which in the past had done so much to retard progress. By late summer the harmful effects of the strike had subsided, and Goethals cabled to the President that 1,274,404 cub. yds. were excavated in August, which was better than any previous record. Roosevelt sent his congratulations, and added, "I am as surprised as I am pleased that you should have surpassed it" when referring to the record. When this interchange of messages was published in the *Canal Record* it made a tremendous impression on the workers and stimulated progress. Moreover, it aroused keen interest throughout the United States, where once again the Canal became headline news.

Goethals came to power at a critical and significant time in the history of the Canal. Preparation of the site for the Gatun Dam began in April, 1907, with one steam-shovel, and the foundations were started in July. Excavation of the Atlantic sea-level channel was started in the dry through the Mindi Hills with steam-shovels, work being made possible by excluding water from the French canal with a dike. Excavation for the locks on the Pacific side and the construction of the relocated Panama Railroad also started about July. Work on the dams and locks rapidly took shape in late summer at both terminals, and masonry work was expected to start on the Gatun Locks within eighteen months. Trestles were under construction for dumping rock along the toes of the dam, the Chagres had been diverted, and pipeline dredgers were at work.

In fact, at this stage of the work construction had gone ahead much faster than had been anticipated. At first, Culebra Cut had been regarded as the critical factor governing the date of completion, then it was the work at the Gatun

Dam, but the latter was in turn dependent on the removal of the old Panama Railroad from the site of the dam to its new location.

The seat of power having been removed to the Isthmus, a further innovation was adopted by Congress when the House Committee on Appropriations arrived at the Isthmus in November, 1907, to hear evidence for the 1909 estimates. They received a welcome from the entire Isthmian Canal Commission. After inspecting the conditions at Cristobal, they were taken on a tour of the Gatun Locks and Dam, the spoil dumps at Tavernilla, then on a trip through the Culebra Cut, over the Pacific locks and dams, to Ancon Hospital and then to Taboga. The next evening they were entertained by a minstrel show at the Culebra Club, the first public entertainment to be given in the Canal Zone.

These Congressmen were very inquisitive. They were critical of the wages and privileges enjoyed by the Canal workers, to whom living quarters had been assigned on the reasonable basis of their salary level. Although the Congressmen were critical during their stay in the Isthmus, when they returned to Washington they reported that conditions in Panama were in excellent shape.

When Goethals went to Washington in January, 1908, he took with him the draft of a proposed Executive Order, prepared with the help of the general counsel, R. R. Rogers. This gave added strength to the order which had been drafted by Stevens, increasing the power of the chairman in appointing heads of departments and adjusting duties amongst the members. When he delivered the draft, Goethals asked Taft to "tell the President that while that's what we'd like, it isn't in accordance with the law", to which Roosevelt made the characteristic reply, "I don't give a damn for the law; I want the Canal built!" and signed the Order on January 6th, 1908. This Order completed the process of centralizing power in the hands of the chairman and chief engineer. The main point was that it put one man in charge of the work, in spite of the refusal of Congress to legislate, and it practically relegated the Commission to a position of impotence.

In December, 1907, the volume of excavation in the Culebra Cut amounted to 1,025,485 cub. yds., and as 1908 dawned there was steady progress on all projects. Plans were afoot for transporting broken rock by barge from the quarry at Porto Bello and sand from Nombre de Dios for the concrete work at Gatun. Rock for the Pacific locks was to be obtained from the quarry at Ancon Hill and sand by barge from Chame. The Cucuracha slide in the Culebra Cut, which had caused the French so much trouble, began to show signs of moving again and threatening the work of the steam-shovels. Goethals expected that more slides would occur later, but he planned to remove them as construction proceeded. He prepared the plant for building the Gatun and Pacific locks, adding to the transport and excavation equipment as required.

The excavation of the Culebra Cut still remains one of the largest pieces of earthwork in the world, and it is this section of the work that may be accurately described as a "canal". The total quantity of excavation, including dredging, for the Panama Canal as originally planned for a lock canal, was estimated to be about 104,000,000 cub. yds., apart from the excavation carried out by the French. Later changes in the original plan increased the volume to about 174,000,000 cub. yds. The total amount excavated by the French engineers was about 81,500,000 cub. yds., including the dredging work at both ends as well as the work in the Culebra Cut, which latter amounted to 22,000,000 cub. yds.

By the end of June, 1908, the Americans had excavated a further 20,000,000 cub. yds. in the Cut, by which name is meant the 9½-mile-long stretch of canal between Bas Obispo and Pedro Miguel. The total quantity to be excavated in the Cut, as calculated at that time, was about 80,000,000 cub. yds. for the high-level canal. The total amount of excavation for the prism of the proposed sea-level canal was calculated by the Board of Consulting Engineers at 231,026,477 cub.

yds. The construction of a sea-level canal along the present Panama route will therefore involve an extremely formidable earthmoving job.

By April, 1910, the excavation had reached a total of 103,000,000 cub. yds., equal to almost the quantity originally estimated for the high-level project. Of the amount excavated by the French, 30,000,000 cub. yds. represented work useful under that plan; the remainder was below a necessary level at the end of the Canal, within the high-level portion.

The plant used in the Culebra Cut included more than a hundred Bucyrus steam-shovels, and over four thousand wagons for the removal of excavated material, the wagons being marshalled in trains and hauled by 160 locomotives of American type and 120 of French type. There were also thirty Lidgerwood unloaders, ploughs of a special type drawn by cable from a winch on the locomotive along the top of the train of flat cars loaded with excavated material, which was thereby discharged to one side in a few minutes. A train of sixteen wagon-loads of rock and earth, containing more than 320 cub. yds. of material, was unloaded by a Lidgerwood unloader in this way in only seven minutes.

Mechanical spreaders in the form of V-shaped ploughs fitted to the front of steam locomotives were used to level the tipped material in the same way as the modern bulldozer, and track shifters were employed to move the track over as an embankment grew. These and many other mechanical devices were made in the local workshops, which were very well equipped. The steam-shovels each had an average output of 1,200 cub. yds. of excavation in an eight-hour day.

Very large quantities of dynamite were used to break up rock so that it could be excavated; shots were fired twice daily, at noon and in the evening, electric firing of the charges being employed. In 1908 dynamite was being used at the rate of more than a million charges a year, and in 1911, at the peak of construction activity, some 10,000,000 lbs. of dynamite were consumed.

The main problem of the Culebra Cut was the rapid

handling and transport of the excavated material to those places where it had to be dumped. Transport was so highly organized that muck-trains followed each other at intervals of three minutes. If they were delayed, the steam-shovels were idle, and although this often occurred at first, with better organization each loaded train was instantly removed to be replaced by a train of empty wagons; this demanded very efficient layout and arrangement of sidings, points and crossings. The shunters and switchmen were West Indian Negroes, who took a keen interest and were proud of their work.

The important problem of landslides was a factor ignored at the outset by the engineers, but the truth was that this could hardly have been foreseen. Slides of earth, but more particularly of rock, added enormously to the work involved in the Culebra Cut. These slides demanded constant change of cross-section of the Canal, and the upper edges of the Cut were taken back far beyond their originally projected lines. As at first designed, the banks of the Cut were comparatively steep, comprising a series of narrow terraces known as berms, alternating with short steep slopes, as it was assumed that the rock would stand at a very steep angle, but this hope was utterly confounded. The International Board of Consulting Engineers decided unanimously that the rock would be stable at a slope of three vertical to two horizontal, and it was considered that this slope could be maintained even in the case of a sea-level canal. It is of interest that this expert body of consultants, European and American, combining the most experienced talent of the time in this particular field of knowledge, estimated the strength of the rock to be such that it would stand at the above slope to a depth of 245 ft. along the centre line, such as a sea-level canal would have required. In fact, however, the rock began to collapse from that slope at a depth of only about 65 ft.

Many test borings had been made and samples of the rock had been brought up before excavation was started, and therefore its quality was known. The reason for the above mistake appears to lie in the fact that some of the underlying strata contained bands of clay and, more importantly, iron pyrites. The latter is liable to become rapidly oxidized on exposure to air and moisture, with the result that the rock will disintegrate. Even the hardest quartz may be split up by this action, which is partly chemical and partly mechanical. Thus, when the upper material had been removed, the rain seeped through to the lower strata and the seams of lignite clay and pyritous material, whereby rapid deterioration resulted. This very action was foreshadowed in the report of one of the French engineers on the International Board, who discovered the friability of the rock when preparing specimens from the test borings for microscopic examination, and therefore had to use oil instead of water when preparing these.

The scheme for carrying out the Cut as recommended by the Board was that the prism with a bottom width of 200 ft. should have slopes of ten vertical to one horizontal to an elevation of 10 ft. above mean tide level, at which elevation there was to be a horizontal berm 50 ft. wide on each side. After this there were to be alternating berms with benches or slopes each 30 ft. high, with a slope of four vertical to one horizontal, the width of the bench at the top being $12\frac{1}{2}$ ft.

The soft material overlying the rock was to have a slope of one vertical to two horizontal. It was revealed in the report that surfaces quite as steep had stood without any sign of collapse since 1889, or for sixteen years, with no evidence of deterioration. Experience showed that the steeper the faces could be, quite apart from the element of crushing, the less they would be likely to deteriorate from rain and climatic changes. Yet the most positive statements made later by American and other engineers as to the stability of the banks were completely disproved in the event.

The first serious slide took place in 1907 at Cucaracha, south of the summit of Gold Hill, where the strata seemed to have been tilted from the horizontal by the upward intrusion of the eruptive rocks forming Gold Hill. The opening crack of this slide was first noted in that year and on October 4th, 1907, without warning, this vast mass of material "shot

6*

almost completely across the Canal, overwhelming two steam-shovels in its course, covering all the railway track, and for ten days maintained a glacier-like movement". The rate of advance of this mass at first was about 14 ft. in 24 hours, decreasing to 4 ft. in the same time after a month. This huge mud landslide completely blocked the Cut with an estimated quantity of 500,000 cub. yds. of material, as much as 30 ft. high in places. It consisted mainly of clay, the overburden above the rock, and it was too soft to be excavated by steam-shovels, or to support the weight of these machines. This great slide was a grave discouragement to all those who worked on the Canal at that time, and there were some who even suggested that it would not be possible to build the Canal at all. The mud was removed by sluicing with water from a high level, followed by removal in trains from the site.

This serious obstacle having been overcome, further movements of rock took place in other parts of the Cut, the most singular feature of which was sudden upheaval of the ground in the bottom of the Cut, at the middle, and a sinking in other parts of the same section. This was due to the pressure or weight of the rock, which tended to flow in the same manner as soil, instead of having the typical behaviour of rock. Movement was stopped by removing material from the upper levels of banks, thereby reducing the pressure. Such slides took place mainly between Empire and Gold Hill, on the east and west banks, the worst portion being about three miles long.

Until the middle of 1908, the Americans had lowered the level of the Cut on the centre line only 10 ft. below the French work, which had brought the bottom to an elevation of 160 ft. above sea level, with 45 ft. of work. The American effort had been concentrated on widening the Cut rather than deepening it, but at that stage of the work an order came from the President to make the bottom width of the Canal at this point 300 ft. instead of the 200 ft. which had first been decided upon. During the following year no further landslides were experienced, but as soon as any deepening was carried out, upheavals and landslides developed to an alarming extent. The terraced slope had been converted into a continuous slope.

In 1910 great slices of the upper bank foundered, and in many places below them the bottom of the Cut bulged upwards by as much as 20 ft., and in one case this movement amounted to 30 ft. This subject has been fully described scientifically in an article by Dr. Vaughan Cornish published in the *Geographical Journal* for March, 1913. The subsidences had a concave surface and the upheavals a convex surface. At one of these "breaks", as they were termed, the first sign of movement was the raising of a steam-shovel working in the Cut, the machine rising about 9 ft. in one afternoon. Such movements had the nature of "gravitational waves", and in another case a steam-shovel rose 11 ft. Elsewhere the upheaval, after having been removed by steam-shovels, appeared again soon afterwards. The material was removed, but the upheaval was repeated again and again, seven times, growing less in size on each occasion.

As a result of these numerous slides and breaks, there was an increase in the volume of excavation, up to June, 1911, of 10,700,000 cub. yds. of material. In order to ensure greater stability or better distribution of weight, the banks of the Cut at these points were again terraced, and a reduction was made in the size of the dynamite charges used. Another serious slide took place in August, 1912, making the twentieth slide, and the total amount of material excavated on account of these movements reached the formidable quantity of 20,000,000 cub. yds.

The flatter slopes of the valley, caused by these excavations, greatly increased the width of the Cut at the top: from 800 to about 2,000 ft. Moreover, as the centre line of the Cut followed the trough of a natural valley, such widening caused the edge to be taken back higher and higher up the slopes, so that the height at Culebra, given originally on the plan as 250 ft. above sea level rose to 315 ft., giving a depth of excavation of 260 ft. Had it been necessary to excavate the Canal to sea level, which would have involved a further 85 ft., it was considered that gigantic slides might have occurred.

At one stage of the work a resident geologist was appointed to help the engineers in their task, but even he was unable to give warning of breaks. The slides were in some cases "dry" and in others "wet", the latter being due partly to the action of rain as described above. In one case so much pyrites was encountered that rapid oxidization owing to moisture took place, and gave off such huge volumes of steam that the workmen thought they had come upon a volcano. A cable message flashed the news abroad and the press announced that "a volcano has burst out in the Canal".

In 1913 the Cucaracha slide became active again, bringing down 2,500,000 cub. yds. of material into the Cut, blocking all the railway tracks and causing the quantity of excavation at that point, owing to slides alone, to reach some 6,000,000 cub. yds. The total amount of excavation for the Culebra Cut after the increase from a bottom width of 200 ft. to one of 300 ft., and including slides, rose to 100,000,000 cub. yds. of material. A revised estimate of the Canal Commission in 1908 had placed the excavation for the Cut at 78,000,000 cub. yds., which rose in 1911 to 94,000,000 and in 1913 to 100,000,000 cub. yds.

There were thus two categories of slides: one due to percolating water and the other to unstable rock formation. In the latter case the steepness and height of the slopes, combined with the effects of blasting, and the removal of lateral support as the material was cut away in the deep parts of the bank, caused the underlying strata to be crushed, and this poor-quality material was unable to sustain the load, being forced upwards from the bottom of the Cut. This type of slide occurred in the dry season and was not due to saturation, being also completely unforeseen. The only remedy was simply to remove the material as it fell. The slides did not in any case delay the progress of the work as a whole, for this was partly determined by the speed with which the locks were constructed.

Living conditions were much improved in spite of some inconveniences. For example, when the tracks of the Panama Railroad in Black Swamp began to sink, the train service was interrupted, with the result that the supply of ice to the line south of the accident was cut off; in Panama the price of this vital commodity increased by 100 per cent. Goethals complained to Congress about the Panamanian merchants, stating that "whenever they can get us in a tight place they squeeze us", but the supplies generally improved throughout the Isthmus. In late April, 1908, the Cristobal bakery was able to deliver "pies, pastry and rolls", and soon afterwards such luxuries as ice-cream were available to the messes along the line of the Canal.

Some idea of the international character of the labour force at work in the Culebra Cut is given by the following description: "The man who ran the steam-shovel, who had charge of the engine and manœuvred it, was an Irishman. The man on the crane, who attended to the dumping, was an American. The two stokers at the engine behind were Jamaican Negroes, and the six members of the 'move up' crew, the men who levelled the ground where the shovel stood and placed the tracks so that it could move forward and keep its nose to the bank, were Sikhs from the north of India, who wore white turbans on their heads and worked like automatons."

There were at this time more than fifty steam-shovels at work in the Culebra Cut, and many projects were getting under way at other parts of the job. The work had been organized in such a manner that the muck-trains took on the appearance of an endless conveyor. Someone who saw what was going on exclaimed: "It's all over but the shouting, gentlemen, barring a few years of work. The Canal will be dug."

The visit of the Appropriations Committee to Culebra in November, 1907, stimulated the desire for effecting economies in the mind of Goethals, who himself was a rare blend of organizer and sound technical expert; unfortunately, these two attainments seldom go together. He had found that the old organization was objectionable because he could not keep as closely in touch with it as he desired. On one occasion he said, "I felt a tendency on the part of some department heads to make the department bigger than the whole." He concluded by saying that the only thing to do was to reorganize, for which he was armed with the Executive Order of January 6th, 1908.

Some trouble developed at the dams at Sosa Hill, and work was suspended pending investigation by Goethals. Then the relocation of the Sosa Locks at Miraflores came as a convenient opportunity to start reorganizing. Goethals created a new unit—the Pacific Division, Lock and Dam Construction. He appointed S. B. Williamson, a civilian friend of long standing, as the divisional engineer. Then he appointed W. G. Comber in charge of all excavation and dredging from Miraflores to the sea. Another move in the plan was the appointment of F. H. Hodges, the general purchasing officer in Washington, to be in charge of the design of the lock gates in addition to his purchasing duties.

In the middle of June, however, Goethals announced the abolition of the Department of Lock and Dam Construction, to be effective from July 1st, and the formation of a new Atlantic Division embracing all the territory north of Tavernilla, to be under Major Sibert as divisional engineer, a change that was to have profound consequences in the future. Ten days later another *Circular* abolished the Department of Excavation and Dredging and formed a Central Division under Major Gaillard, with L. K. Rourke as assistant divisional engineer. A third *Circular* announced the formation of the Pacific Division under S. B. Williamson. This completed the final reorganization into major construction divisions— the Atlantic, the Central and the Pacific. Other changes followed. The Department of Motive Power and Machinery, Municipal Engineering, and Building Construction was distributed among the three main construction divisions.

With the *Canal Record* publishing excavation figures every week, the organization was ideal for the development of friendly rivalry between divisions, between steam-shovels and between men. The organization was unusual, too, in that army engineers were in complete control on the Atlantic side; civilians ruled on the Pacific side; and in the Central Division there was a combination of civilian and military rule. The final boundaries of the main construction divisions were fixed by natural features: the Central Division extended from the south end of Gatun Locks to the north end of Pedro Miguel, the Atlantic Division included everything to the north, and the Pacific Division everything to the south.

Goethals used this reorganization as an ideal opportunity to grade the members of his staff and to discharge those who did not measure up to the high standard that he set. The reorganization of the Medical Department proved to be beneficial, for expenses were reduced and there was also a reduction in the number of nurses and doctors employed.

In Congress there was a move to re-create the office of Governor of the Canal Zone, a political appointment. One Congressman asked why Goethals, as chairman, should be superior in authority. Goethals replied, "I do not see how we are going to operate here unless someone is vested with authority to step in and decide questions." The Congressman continued to press Goethals on this point. He was asked about the possibility of conflict with his duties if there were some other co-ordinator. He answered, "It did prior to my coming, and I presume it would while I remain here."

The reorganization revealed the exceptional administrative capacity of this outstanding man, although it was of course a natural outcome of previous arrangements. It gave the job three chief engineers of construction—Sibert, Gaillard and Williamson, freeing Goethals from much irritating detail and enabling him to concentrate on larger issues. As can be imagined, he was a hard taskmaster, holding his subordinates responsible for results and, as he himself said, "I do not impose the employment of any man on any division engineer.

I let them select their forces, and hold them strictly responsible." His men soon learned that he was both strict and just, being familiar with government routine and knowing how to secure practical results in spite of it. Moreover, he proved to be highly skilled when it came to dealing with Congressional Committees, which he did in a direct and forceful manner.

During the first years of Canal construction by the Americans there were many changes. The planners had not by any means foreseen everything. The general plan for a lock canal, as adopted by Congress, included two sites for locks on the Pacific side, one at Pedro Miguel and the other near Sosa Hill, an arrangement that provided a large intermediate level lake for the Pacific terminal. Work originally started on the dams under Stevens, but he did not like this scheme because the Sosa site was too near the coast from a defence point of view, and would be vulnerable to gunfire from ships in the bay. He had explored the area and taken test borings to determine the strata; he had chosen a site at Agua Dulce, south of Miraflores, but his proposal had not been adopted. He also proposed that the Pacific locks should be combined in a single structure, which would in his opinion improve the Canal plan, but this again was not adopted.

Under the direction of Goethals, construction of the dams on Sosa Lake went ahead. One night a trestle fell over and the embankment being tipped from it subsided 8 ft. When a train passed over the next morning, the track sank 6 ft. The work was stopped immediately, and Goethals started an investigation that included test borings from La Boca to Pedro Miguel, in order to find a suitable foundation. He also appointed a board to make a report on the sites for locks. Three projects were studied—first, a single-lift lock at Pedro Miguel and a two-lift lock at La Boca; second, a two-lift lock at Pedro Miguel and a single-lift one at Miraflores; and third, a single-lift lock at each of these three sites. They considered all combinations and recommended one lift at Pedro Miguel and two lifts at Miraflores.

Goethals considered the idea of building all the locks together at Miraflores, but this would have required a vast concrete foundation, the cost of which would have been prohibitive. He reported to the President on December 9th, 1907, in favour of one lift at Pedro Miguel and two at Miraflores, an arrangement that enabled the Panama Railroad terminals at La Boca to be used without interruption. These proposals were approved by the President, to the great satisfaction of the engineers concerned, who had been struggling with a very difficult problem.

A further important change was in the dimensions of locks. The Canal plan had called for locks 95 ft. wide, but the President in his message of December 3rd, 1907, expressed the opinion that the locks should be 120 ft. wide. The United States Navy requested that the width should be increased to 110 ft. to take the largest battleship then planned, which was to have a beam of 100 ft., but Goethals doubted whether the Navy would build ships requiring a lock of greater width than 100 ft. The Commission recommended the change proposed by the Navy, and the President approved this on January 15th, 1908, but there were many people who considered that locks 110 ft. wide were too narrow. It is of interest to record that a few years later, in 1912, when Goethals was visiting the Kiel Canal, Kaiser Wilhelm told him that the Panama Canal locks should have been wider. That crafty old strategist knew what he was talking about, but by then it was too late.

The earth and rock from the gigantic Culebra Cut had to be transported by rail to the site of the Gatun Dam, some 30 miles distant from the Cut. This huge dam contains nearly 21,000,000 cub. yds. of material; its construction was at one period subjected to a great deal of discussion and criticism. To the untrained eye the dam appears to present little evidence of the enormous amount of work put into it, an impression given by many works of civil engineering construction. This great structure is covered by a great mass of tropical vegetation which, as it is protective, has been permitted. At one time there was a great deal of apprehension about the work, mainly caused by sensational but imaginative reports in the press that "the dam was sinking into an underground lake", owing to some slight displacement of the edge of the bank.

On the Pacific side of the Canal a considerable volume of excavation was carried out by hydraulicking, which consisted of washing down the bank with powerful jets of water under high pressure, after the manner of the monitors used in the China clay pits of Cornwall. This process, under the right conditions, will separate soils from stones with remarkable speed. The flushed material flows into a pool or sump below the bank and is then forced through steel pipes by centrifugal dredging pumps of large output, being conveyed for considerable distances to the site where it is desired to deposit the material.

From the engineering point of view, the locks and their equipment were probably the most important works on the Canal. There are twelve of these in all: a double flight of three on the Atlantic side, and double flights of two and one on the Pacific side. Each lock consists in the main of a huge chamber 1,000 ft. long and 110 ft. wide, with walls and a floor of concrete, and watertight steel gates at each end. The side walls vary in thickness from 45 to 50 ft. at floor level, perpendicular on the lock face, narrowing on the land side to a top width of 8 ft. The central wall between the parallel flights is 60 ft. thick, 81 ft. high, with vertical faces. At a point 42 ft. above the surface of the floor runs a tunnel longitudinally through this great wall, divided into three storeys, the lowest being for drainage, the middle one for the cables operating the gate and valve machinery, within the wall, and the upper serving as a passage for the operators. The locks are filled and emptied by several lateral culverts, discharging upwards in the floors, which connect with main culverts, 18 ft. in diameter, running through the walls. Water enters and flows through the locks under the action of gravity.

The full length of each lock does not necessarily have to be used for the passage of every vessel. In order to lock the smaller vessels through, and also to save both time and water, intermediate gates have been fitted in the lock chambers, dividing these into locks of 600 and 400 ft. length respectively. The maximum lift of the Panama Canal locks is 32 ft. and the width 110 ft., the gates being of the type known as mitre gates, and the total number of single gates is 92 for the whole Canal. Each gate leaf is a steel structure of immense strength, 7 ft. thick and 65 ft. long, the height varying from 47 to 82 ft., and the weight from 300 to 600 tons each. In order to take the weight off the top hinge and bottom pivot supporting the gates, they have been made with watertight and airtight compartments, so that they have a considerable amount of buoyancy and the weight is therefore diminished.

The proposed siting and location of the Gatun locks was heavily criticized at an early stage of the American activities, for the main reason that part of the foundation would rest upon material other than rock. More than 2,000,000 cub. yds. of concrete were used in the construction of the Gatun locks, and the total volume of concrete used for all the locks amounted to 4,500,000 cub. yds. The floors of all locks are of reinforced concrete.

Great care is taken in operating the Canal locks. Any vessel arriving at either end of the Canal is given over to the navigational control of the Canal authorities, whose representative takes charge on the bridge of the ship, with another representative in the engine-room. The ship is towed through each lock by electric locomotives running on railway track and known as "mules"; there are two on each side of the ship at the bow and at the stern. They run with a centre rack rail, and are fitted with a slip drum so that the towing hawsers can be hauled in or paid out without actual motion of the locomotive along the track, if desired. In passing from the elevation of one lock to that of another, these locomotives climb and descend short, sharp gradients at an angle of about twenty-two degrees with the horizontal.

Strict precautions are taken against overrunning. Before

a ship enters a lock, a chain is stretched across the entrance. This chain is dropped into a groove at the bottom of the channel if all is clear, but if the ship is moving too rapidly, the great chain remains stretched so that the vessel will run against it. The chain is operated at the ends by hydraulic machinery in the walls, designed to stop a ship of 10,000 tons, travelling at a speed of 4 m.p.h., in a distance of 73 ft., which is less than the distance between the chain and and first lock gate.

In locking a ship through the Gatun locks, four fender chains have to be operated; six pairs of gates must be opened and shut; and eight pairs of valve gates and thirty cylindrical valves opened, admitting water through the culverts to float the ship upwards. A total of 98 electric motors are set in motion twice during the lockage of a single ship, which may be increased to 143 motors, according to circumstances. The time required to pass a vessel through the locks is estimated to be about one and a half hours at each end, with a total for the Canal of ten to twelve hours, depending upon the size and speed of the vessel. The system of operating the locks has been made interlocking in order to avoid the risk of human error, the individual parts of the installation being controlled in various phases, designed to provide maximum safety. A separate motor operates each gate, valve and fender chain.

In a building above the locks there is a control board, 64 ft. long, with a complete model of the locks and their apparatus, in which the water actually rises and falls, and the gates and chains operate in miniature. The operator directs and controls the passage of vessels from this tower. A special machine was invented by Panama Canal engineers for opening and closing the lock gates and this equipment was put to a supreme test by being used to operate the gates without any water in the Canal. The heavy lock gates, weighing from 400 to 700 tons each, can be opened and closed each way in about two minutes.

In addition to the safeguards provided against accidental ramming of the gates, there is a further device known as an emergency dam, which takes the form of a steel truss bridge of cantilever type. This has been designed in such a manner that it can be swung across the entrance to the lock in only two minutes, and should a gate be destroyed and the lower locks be flooded—an emergency that could be disastrous— this dam can be lowered to stop the flow.

The overflow spillway to the Gatun Dam takes the form of an arc of a circle, 1,200 ft. long and 85 ft. wide, cut through the centre of the dam, with the convex side towards the lake. This massive concrete structure contains 140,000 cub. yds. of material, rising to a height of 69 ft. above sea level, thereby reaching to 16 ft. below the 85-ft. level of the lake. The thirteen concrete piers reach a height of 115·5 ft. above sea level at their crest, and the steel sluice gates between them, which regulate the level of the lake, are raised and lowered by machinery, sliding on trains of rollers in niches. The discharge capacity of the spillway was calculated to be greater than the known maximum discharge of the Chagres River under flood conditions.

The dams at Pedro Miguel and Miraflores are small in comparison with that at Gatun. Their foundations are upon solid rock, and are subject to pressure from a head of 40 ft. of water, instead of 80 ft. as at Gatun. If there should be a breakage of the top lock gate at Gatun, as well as of the emergency gates, thus allowing the water of the lake to escape into the Atlantic, the depth of the lake would still remain 32 ft. near the dam. The volume of this lake is so large, in fact, that it would be lowered by only 2 ft. per day, so that more than three weeks would pass before the waters reached that level. Such conditions do not obtain at the other dams. If the water escaped, vessels would be stranded and a dangerous current would be generated.

Any lock-type canal requires a constant supply of water to replenish that used for the operation of locking. As ships pass through the locks a considerable volume of water, equal to the volume contained in each lock between its high and low level, will be lost, and if the higher portion of the canal did not receive a further supply, after a time it would run dry. The replenishment of the waters of Lake Gatun was one of the main problems studied when the high-level canal was being designed. This lake is supplied by the Chagres River, which, in the dry season, has a comparatively insignificant flow, although it rises to a great flood in the rainy season. When this river is low, the local inhabitants make use of the dry bed where possible instead of a road, but during about eight months of the year the lake is kept constantly full by the prevailing rains, so that the necessary surplus has to be stored for only a few months.

The operating machinery for the Canal is powered by water turbines, the water passing from the lake through a culvert near the north wall of the spillway. The turbines provide power for the lock-operating machinery, machine shops and repair plants, the dry dock, lighting and operating locomotives on the Panama Railroad.

A change introduced by Goethals was the building of a breakwater from La Boca to Naos Island, with the aim of preventing silting of the channel. When the dump at La Boca was started, the idea of extending it in the form of a breakwater to Naos Island was natural. In spite of the wide tidal range in the Pacific, water near the island was always deep enough for shipping, regardless of the state of the tide, but in La Boca ships could be handled only at high tide. Later there came a change in the west breakwater at Colon, which was relocated to run from Toro Point eastwards across Limon Bay to the channel instead of running parallel to the latter as originally intended by the Commission. This change made it possible to complete the breakwater protection of the harbour by building an eastern breakwater.

The Canal plan demanded a bottom width of 200 ft. in the Culebra Cut, but as the rocky sides could damage the hulls of ships, it was necessary to increase this width in order to prevent sinkings, more particularly of the larger vessels. Goethals recommended a bottom width of 300 ft. and this was approved by the President. These changes increased the cost of the Canal, which Goethals estimated would be 250,000,000 dollars.

For a long time the work at Gatun Dam had been a subject of controversy. After work had started, a newspaper reporter visiting the Isthmus wrote an alarming article about an underground lake at the site, a story that was widely believed by those not familiar with the facts. Later, in November, 1908, after a spell of heavy rain, part of the rock filling in the upstream toe of the dam slid, but this was a comparatively minor happening. However, as bad luck would have it, another reporter happened to be crossing the Isthmus by train at the time. Whilst viewing the sights at Gatun, he observed the flood water and the dent made by the slide. With his weather eye on a good headline he cabled to the United States another alarming story—that Gatun Dam was being destroyed by falling into an underground lake! This news created a national sensation and the dam became a political issue.

Fortunately, however, *Engineering News* of December 24th published an editorial defending the Canal authorities and emphasizing the stability of the dam. Stevens generously rushed to the defence of his friend Goethals in an open letter published in that journal the following week, condemning this outbreak of sensational journalism. He admitted that when the dam was designed 25 ft. had been added to the height, and both toes had been unduly enlarged as a "concession to prejudice" but went on to say that he had intended to reduce the cross-section of the dam later during construction. Even Congress entered the battle, and sent a committee once more to investigate the affairs of the Canal. The members were naturally inquisitive about the dam, but Goethals was ready for them. At last, when asked if he had consulted fully and freely with his associates, he replied, "Always—not only with the division engineers, but lower down. I will consult a foreman about his particular class of work. It helps the foreman and it helps me."

The scheme to combine the Pacific locks was still being actively debated, and Sibert had revived the subject by submitting a definite plan. He wanted to have an anchorage space above the locks in what is now Miraflores Lake, so that ships leaving the Canal at Pedro Miguel could anchor safely, a plan that would have improved operation of the Canal. Congress became interested and the proposal was examined by a Board which had recommended the combination of the Pacific locks, but Goethals thought that this combination would seriously delay the opening of the Canal. He wanted to press on with the work, but as the plant for two locks had been ordered, a change would have entailed a long delay.

The fundamental errors in the design of the Panama Canal were the failure to create a summit-level anchorage between Culebra Cut and the Pacific locks, and the failure to build the Pacific locks as single structures. However, it should be said in defence of the designers that the Panama Canal was at that time under fire by politicians and the public. Perhaps no other course was open to them, but there is no evidence available to prove that the designers explained the reasons for making the changes with adequate force and clarity. It is easy to see mistakes with the benefit of hindsight.

There was progress on all sides since the reorganization. The Canal Medals, promised by the President in November, 1906, had arrived and acted as a powerful incentive for renewed effort, because they were highly prized by the employees. On one side the Medal bore a portrait of the President, and on the other a view of the finished Culebra Cut, with vessels passing through the artificial rocky gorge between Gold Hill and Contractors Hill. Inscribed "For two years' continuous service on the Panama Canal" and "Presented by the President of the United States", with the employee's name inscribed beneath the shield of Panama, the Medal was a great encouragement.

The Panama Canal was an outstanding example of a very large work of construction undertaken under what can only be described as an autocratic régime, and a great deal of valuable administrative experience was gained thereby. Americans have always been highly individualistic, but it was clear from the outset that tenders submitted by conventional civilian contractors were not satisfactory, and they had to be rejected. Moreover, experience proved only too conclusively that administration of the work by a commission of seven was quite hopeless, because the various authorities concerned were subjected to strong political pressures and were unduly influenced by the popular demand to "make the dirt fly". It was absolutely vital that there should be one absolute boss for this great work, and nobody could have been more suitable than Goethals.

Both President Roosevelt and Mr. Taft, Secretary for War, were profoundly convinced that the work should be carried out under the overall direction of a military engineer. In the event, this type of administration ensured that the vast sums spent were managed with maximum economy combined with efficiency. It was stated at the time that the whole operation moved "swiftly and with precision, directed by one mind and free from the disturbance of conflicting purposes".

One of the main lessons learnt from this work was the vital need for good and plentiful food, a fact clearly evident in the treatment of the large number of West Indian Negroes employed. In 1906 the Commission was deeply dissatisfied with the work of these men, many of whom had worked under the French régime, and it was reported that "another year's experience with Negro labourers from nearby tropical islands and countries, has convinced the Commission of the impossibility of doing satisfactory work with them. Not only do they seem to be disqualified by lack of actual vitality, but their disposition to labour seems to be as frail as their bodily strength".

This unsatisfactory state of affairs was due to two causes. The more important was the lack of sufficient food, yet curiously enough it was some time before this primitive condition was discovered. Food eaten by the Negroes was of bad quality and insufficient quantity. The remedy was to provide them with properly cooked meals, of the same type as those supplied to American and European workers. In order to ensure that they should profit by this provision, the charge for meals was deducted from their wages. The aim was to ensure that the men would be properly fed rather than to make any profit out of the catering.

The cost of providing messes for European and Negro workers was given in a report in 1909, which stated that for six months of that year the cost amounted to 719,000 dollars, as against 716,000 dollars for takings from the sale of meals. In 1907 the number of meals served reached nearly one million per month, and rose steeply thereafter. At that time there were many hotels for white Americans thus controlled, where wholesome meals were provided at a cost of 30 cents a head, equivalent in those days to 1s. 3d.; and for European labourers, where a day's board cost only 40 cents. There were also many kitchens for the West Indian workers with the day's board at 30 cents. The excellent quality of the Government kitchens was proved by the fact that out of 4,800 European labourers, who were free to eat where they wished, 3,400 preferred the official mess-halls.

Under this system, much more favourable accounts were heard of the West Indian contribution to the construction of the Canal, the Negroes becoming much stronger and working with a better will. In the past, most of them had subsisted on a handful of bananas or other inadequate food. At that time the daily wage of a Negro in Barbados was about a shilling during the short sugar harvest season, but on the Canal work he earned 10 cents, or about 5d., an hour, with a daily deduction of only 30 cents for three good meals. His lodgings were both sanitary and free.

Experience proved that the British West Indian Negroes eventually formed the most valuable labour force on the Canal. Before this desirable state of affairs was reached, however, the importation of several thousand Chinese workmen was contemplated but not carried out. Improved working conditions also had the effect of stimulating recruitment of European labour from such countries as Greece, Italy and Spain. The Spaniards and Italians were found to be physically superior to the Greeks; many of the Italians were migrants, part of the floating population of Latin America. They were of excellent physical capacity, but they did give some trouble by their ability for collective action if they were not satisfied with conditions, and as a result their numbers were somewhat reduced. The Spaniards were mainly from Galicia and Castile, and at certain periods of the work they made up about five-sixths of the European labour. These men generally worked very well together because they came directly from their villages, were quick to learn, patient and generally well behaved. Furthermore, they appeared to be able to withstand the rigours of tropical heat better than any workmen of northern race.

From all accounts, Colonel Goethals had a very high reputation in the management and control of his huge labour force. He established a kind of open court on Sundays, at which he heard informally any complaints brought to him by employees, quite independently of their status or race. The white skilled men included mechanics, who performed their duties with enthusiasm, often inspired by the example set by the chief engineer. The white employees, however, were constantly changing and many of them returned to America at certain stages of the work.

Full recognition was accorded to trade unions throughout the Canal works, and an eight-hour day was adopted. The American mechanics, such as the drivers of steam-shovels and other important machines, were employed on what came to be known as the "gold roll", and they generally received 65 cents an hour. The trade unions played a very important part in negotiating the wages and conditions of this class of labour, and it was largely due to union action that no Chinese workers were imported on a large scale into the Canal Zone.

Although there were accidents and deaths on this immense

work, every possible effort was made to encourage safety. Landslides were the main cause of disaster, and these became increasingly frequent towards the end of the work. There were also several train accidents, and dynamite explosions also occurred. In one case, already referred to, in June 1912 a steam-shovel at work in the Culebra Cut was overwhelmed by a mass of rock and soil from the bank above its working site. Fortunately, however, the men operating the machine saw the danger, and were lucky to escape with their lives. So severe was this landslide that the machine was completely wrecked.

The roughly laid temporary tracks for the muck-trains caused a good deal of jolting and men were thrown off at times, railway accidents having been responsible for 150 deaths. Considering the size of the labour force, this cannot be regarded as a high figure. Although explosions also caused accidents, it was claimed that the percentage of deaths from this cause was lower on the Canal than on other large works then being undertaken. In using some 10,000,000 lbs. of dynamite during the year 1911 only ten lives were lost. In 1909, however, a charge of 44,000 lbs. of dynamite, which had been charged into fifty-three holes at Bas Obispo in the Culebra Cut, exploded prematurely and caused twenty-six deaths and several injuries. At another place some 12 tons of dynamite exploded, claimed to have been due to the effect of a flash of lightning, and eight men were killed.

Considering that at the peak period of construction there was a labour force of 85,000 men at work, accidents were inevitable, but the comparatively low death-rate was largely due to the fact that this was a Government project, on which safety precautions were rigidly enforced. It was estimated in 1911 that by the middle of 1913 the labour force in the Canal Zone would be reduced to 20,000 men, but near this date there were still 40,000 men at work every day; of these, 30,000 were West Indian Negroes, 4,000 were Spaniards, and there were 6,000 white Americans employed in administrative and commercial posts.

The mixed character of the labour force may be judged by the figures for the town of Empire, in which there were 7,000 inhabitants in 1912; these included 1,700 Whites, some 4,000 Negroes, 1,500 mestizos, a hundred Chinamen and twenty-five East Indians, with a small number of Arabs, Syrians and others. On the outskirts of the town there were Spanish *cantinas*, American "saloons", Chinese shops, and Negro tailors and shoemakers. Beyond this fringe of civilization were those who preferred a half-jungle life of relative independence, dwelling in huts that were in striking contrast to the orderly aspect of the town and its surroundings.

Generally speaking, the main labour force consisted of British, American and Spanish workers. In 1912, at the peak period of construction, 75 per cent of the workers were Negroes, British West Indian subjects, with Americans, Spaniards and a few Italians. From the year 1906 onwards, Americans represented about one-seventh of the total labour force, another seventh consisted of European workers, and the rest were West Indian Negroes. Constant recruitment was necessary to maintain the labour force at the necessary strength; half the arrivals were engaged by agents, and half came to the Zone on their own account.

With all the construction forces in full swing, progress in the Culebra Cut went ahead by leaps and bounds. Spoil was carried to the dumps on the main line at Tavernilla, at Gatun Dam, La Boca, the Naos Island breakwater and to a few intermediate ones. Rock from the Porto Bello quarries and sand from Nombre de Dios for the concrete work at Gatun were towed in barges by powerful tugs up the old French channel to their destination. On the Pacific side of the Canal, rock for lock building came from Ancon quarry and sand was towed from Chame to La Boca. Cement was brought by railway steamers *Ancon* and *Cristobal* from the United States.

Dredgers operated on the sea-level sections of the Canal, and at La Boca a new channel was being dredged to the west of Naos Island, parallel to the breakwater. Some of the dredgers picked up pieces of eight and cannon-balls more than three centuries old. On this channel, equipment left behind by the French was still working. On February 1st, 1909, the first five miles of the Panama Canal were completed, an event celebrated by two Pacific Mail steamers entering La Boca harbour to the accompaniment of ships' whistles. In a few days the old French channel was closed by the Naos breakwater. Fig. 8 is an outline sketch of two American dipper dredgers employed on underwater excavation.

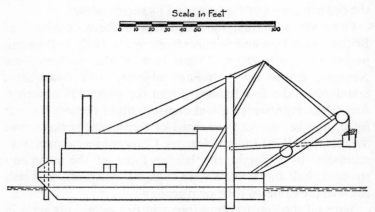

8. *The steam-dipper dredgers* Gamboa *and* Paraiso, *both of the same design*

At this period, the Culebra Cut was the most dramatic sight on the Canal works, for it covered about nine miles of intense activity, with the steam-shovels operating on terraces. The danger of slides was ever present during construction, and these still occur today. A visitor described the most impressive sight of the Canal, which was the view from the bottom of the artificial gorge between Gold Hill and Contractors Hill. To both north and south one could see "a swarming mass of men and rushing railway trains, monster-like machines, all working with ceaseless activity, all animated seemingly by human intelligence, without confusion or conflict anywhere". Empty trains entered the Cut on a rising gradient to the summit, backing from there to the steam-shovels, where they were loaded and then hauled away to the dump. There they were rapidly unloaded by special machines that pushed the spoil off the flat cars, and it was then levelled by inclined blades fixed to the front of steam locomotives with an action similar to that of the modern bulldozer. As the embankments were dumped, the track was lifted and slewed over to a new alignment by machines that were simply mobile cranes.

The steam-shovel crews worked for eight hours per day, from 7 to 11 a.m. and from 1 to 5 p.m. At the end of the day's work, the locomotives were taken to sidings for repair and overhaul, and during the night shift, service trains ran through the Cut with supplies of coal and water for the shovels and track-shifters. At about 6.30 every morning sixty steam locomotives would pull out of the sidings, coupled to trains of from twenty to thirty flat cars, to start another day's work in the endless chain of dump cars travelling between the shovels and the dumps.

Protection of the Culebra Cut against interruption was a very important matter, for the flood water at the Chagres River rose high enough at Gamboa to enter the excavated Cut. To prevent what might have been a disaster, the Cut was protected from this river by a dike at Gamboa 78 ft. above sea level. By August, 1909, the Culebra Cut at Obispo was down to the full depth of 40 ft. above sea level; at the continental divide it was 120 ft. above sea level, with an excavation rate of 1,200,000 cub. yds. a month and 42,332,400 cub. yds. remaining to be removed. This problem had been solved.

In 1910 work on the Chagres section of the Central Division was suspended, and the men were moved to increase the labour force at work on track relocation. Forty-two shovels were at work in the Culebra Cut, but this number had to be reduced as the excavation deepened and narrowed. By November, 1911, more than 70,942,244 cub. yds. had been excavated, and only 18,501,761 remained to be removed. It was expected that excavation would be finished in January, 1913.

The great task now facing Goethals was to ensure that the various projects on the Canal would be completed in the required sequence. He had to appear before a Committee of Congress each year to obtain funds. At the start of each year he gave a summary of the Canal organization, reviewed the work in progress and indicated the degree of completion.

Two events of local interest occurred during 1909. The Peruvian Minister to Panama, following the precedent of naming Cristobal and Colon after the discoverer of the New World, suggested that the Pacific terminal of the Canal should bear the name of the discoverer of the Pacific. This suggestion was adopted, and the name of the Pacific port was changed from La Boca to Balboa by direction of the President. Ex-President Amador of Panama died on May 2nd, 1909, only a few months after the end of his term of office. The next day all work on the Canal stopped for five minutes at 4 p.m., the time of the funeral. Taft, then on the Isthmus, wrote a letter of sympathy to the Panama Government and announced that the fortifications of the Pacific would be named Fort Amador, after the founder of the Republic of Panama.

In spite of many distractions at this time, Goethals pushed on with the work. Construction of the Gatun Dam began on the east sector, an arrangement that forced the Chagres to the westward of Spillway Hill, through the old French West Diversion, which was left open to prevent its waters from backing up the river valley. The dam and spillway were ready to be closed in April, 1910, when hundreds of car-loads of spoil were dumped into the West Diversion, and at 5 p.m. on April 25th, the flow of the River Chagres past Gatun ceased and Gatun Lake began to form. When Goethals made his progress report for October 31st, 1910, the Atlantic sea-level sector was 57·4 per cent complete; 42 per cent of the concrete had been poured at Gatun Lock; the Gatun Dam

Above, the W.1800 walking dragline excavator in use on opencast coal mining at Maesgwyn, South Wales; *below*, an excavating bucket of 40 cubic yards in the Hadfields works

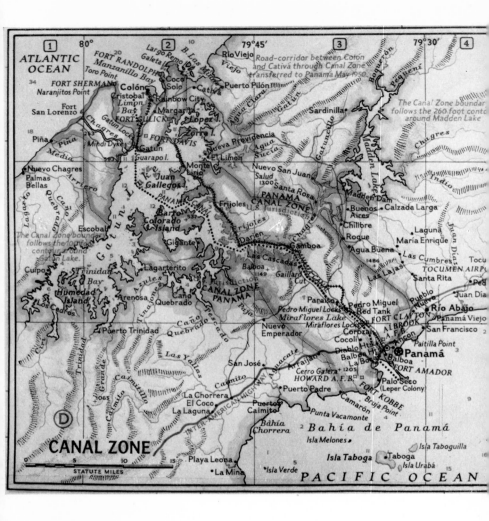

· · · · · Route of Panama Canal   +++++++++ Panama Railroad

Elevations in feet   Soundings in fathoms

(*By courtesy of the National Geographic Magazine*)

was 53·8 per cent complete, and the Central Division was 67·5 per cent finished. Pedro Miguel Locks were 35·2 per cent complete, but Miraflores only 4·7 per cent; the Pacific sea-level sector had been 71·7 per cent completed. Relocation of the track was going ahead, and it was expected that the level of the Gatun Lake would be 55 ft. above sea level after January, 1912.

Taft, now President of the United States, visited the Isthmus in November, 1910. Escorted by Colonel Goethals, he started on his inspection across the Isthmus. They stopped at Monte Lirio, known locally as Mitchellville after Mike Mitchell the station-master, who had become friendly with Goethals. The President, feeling the heat, was offered iced tea by Mitchell and gladly accepted it. "They tell me you are quite a big shot around here," remarked Mr. Taft to his host, to which the latter replied, "You bet your big fat stern I am"; Goethals was taken aback, but Taft laughed heartily and was much amused by this welcome break in tropical monotony.

A labour crisis came to a head while Goethals was in Washington about February, 1911. A locomotive driver who was drunk on duty passed a signal and crashed into the rear of a freight train, killing a man. The driver was sentenced to twelve months' imprisonment for manslaughter, but the locomotive and shovel drivers took exception to this. A group of fifty of them visited Colonel Hedges' home in Culebra and demanded the man's unconditional release, under threat to strike. Hodges, at that time acting chairman and chief engineer, refused, and advised the men to wait until Goethals returned.

On his return he was told of the situation, and awaited developments for which he was quite prepared in the light of past experience. The time-limit set by the men approached and on the evening of the day that it expired a spokesman phoned Goethals at his home and demanded to know what he intended to do about the ultimatum. Goethals replied, "I have three things to say. First, I am not in the habit of being

7

dictated to over the telephone. Second, I am not going to grant it, and last, anyone not at work at seven in the morning will be sent off the Isthmus in the next boat." The men were on the job ahead of time next morning, and the incident was closed.

The year 1911 saw the peak of the Canal work, and when Goethals appeared before a Congressional Committee he was applauded for the first time and praised by the chairman. He reported that the steel lock gates would be completed in January, 1913, and that the locks should therefore be finished, ready to receive the gates by October, 1912. He expected the Culebra Cut to be completed by September, 1913, but held to January 1st, 1915, as the opening date for the Canal, because he wanted to organize the canal operating force and test the machinery.

By December, 1911, the concrete work of the Pacific Locks was 87 per cent complete, and it was expected that the whole Pacific Division would reach completion by June, 1913. There was similar progress at Gatun and in the Culebra Cut. At that time there were no military forces in the Canal Zone, except for a small detachment of Marines, but planners of the Federal Government were studying problems of defence, and an Interdepartmental Fortification Board visited the Isthmus for discussions in 1910. One member of the Board expressed fear of the danger of bombing, at the time in very early stages of development, and Goethals replied, "I haven't the faith in the airship that you have." When asked how much land would be required for defence purposes, Goethals said, "I can only state that when the fortification board was here in 1910 and outlined the land required by the Army and Navy I began to question if after the Army and Navy got through there would be enough land left to provide for construction of the canal."

Early in 1913 the builders of the Canal saw the end of the job in sight. There were thirty-seven steam-shovels at work in the Culebra Cut, concrete was being poured at Gatun and Miraflores Locks, the Gatun Lake was rising and was expected to reach 50 ft. above sea level by July and its final level of 85 ft. above sea level by December. The Gamboa Dike across the north end of Culebra Cut was 78 ft. above sea level and protected it from the rising waters of the Chagres. Because the lake was expected to reach a level of 74 ft. above sea level by about October 10th, the dike would not serve its purpose much longer. A dike across the Pacific channel south of Miraflores Locks protected these locks from the waters of the Pacific.

The greatest potential danger of all, which could delay the scheduled completion of the whole work, was the Cucuracha slide in the Culebra Cut, and it was this slide that Robert Fowler saw when he made the first flight over the Canal on April 27th, 1913. Early in May it became clear that the Culebra Cut would have to be completed by dredging after flooding, the Cut having remained to the very end as the main problem of the Canal. To prepare for the work, Goethals placed all dredging equipment and operations under the direction of W. G. Comber, in the Sixth Division of the Chief Engineer's Office, which was later to become the Dredging Division.

The Cucuracha slide proved to be a difficult problem. When it started to move in January, 1913, it crossed the Cut until it reached the opposite bank. At first the shovels attacking it could make no headway, but gradually a working space was cleared for trucks, and was kept open by constant excavation as the slide advanced. There was no interruption elsewhere in the Cut as the steam-shovels approached each other in the last lap of the work. At 4.30 p.m. on May 20th, 1913, to the accompaniment of steam-whistles and cheers from the workers, the meeting of the shovels occurred opposite Hodges Hill.

During this time of record output in the Culebra Cut, Colonel Gaillard, Divisional Engineer of the Central Division, suffered a breakdown of health, and his doctor advised him to give up all work and to seek a change of climate and surroundings. He went on leave but was retained as a member of the Commission. Activity in Culebra Cut continued unabated until September 10th, on which day all excavation in the Cut ended. Pumps that had kept the Cut dry were removed, track was lifted, old sleepers were burned and houses salvaged.

The first operation of the Canal locks took place on September 26th at Gatun, where thousands of people came to see the tests, and lined the lock walls as Goethals paced nervously up and down. The lake was up to the 65·5 ft. level above the sea instead of at the normal operating level of 85 ft. Water was admitted to the upper chamber and sluiced down by stages to the lowest level. The tug *Gatun* was locked up in three steps to the summit level in 1 hr. 51 min., and then *Gatun* entered the lake, an event hailed around the world as indicating the approaching completion of the Canal. The locking up of the Atlantic dredging fleet on its way to the Culebra Cut followed on October 9th, and these lockages were up to the same standard.

The final rise of Gatun Lake had started when the last spillway gates were closed on June 27th, with the water level at 48·25 ft. above sea level, the level of 85 ft. being expected by December. On July 1st the level was at 50 ft. Gorgona was evacuated and the workshops were removed to Balboa. In October heavy rains caused a rapid rise, and the old town of Cruces was therefore abandoned. Plans for the new town of Balboa were started and the decision was taken to abandon Culebra, Empire and other towns on the west bank of the Canal which would be isolated when the Cut was flooded. On October 1st, drain-pipes in the Gamboa Dike were opened in order partly to fill the Cut in advance, because of the danger from so much flowing water.

For ten days dynamite charges were placed in the dike as the level of the lake slowly rose. The day finally arrived, and three thousand people gathered to see the union of the two great oceans. Amongst them was the French engineer Philippe Bunau-Varilla, who had come to witness the culmination of what had been his own ambition. In Washington at 2 p.m. on October 10th, 1913, President Woodrow Wilson pressed a key on his desk which fired the charges at Gamboa and opened the dike. Water rushed through the opening from the lake at the 67·7-ft. level to the 61·6-ft. level of the Cut, starting a wave in the Cut that reached the Cucuracha slide in 18 minutes. South of the slide the Cut was dry.

Water had to be passed through the slide to the dry part of the Cut so that dredgers could be locked up from the Pacific, and charges were placed in the slide to make a breach. Late on the same afternoon they were exploded but they were not effective, and the only result was that the spectators were spattered with mud and soil. Men had to dig a trench in the slide through which to flood the remaining section of the Cut. On that same day the Central Division was abolished and only the Atlantic Division remained. Water from the Pacific reached Miraflores Locks when the dike there was blown up on August 31st, and the lake was gradually filled. By the middle of October it had reached the 37-ft. level as compared with the normal level of 55 ft. above sea level. The first lockage through these locks was for the tug *Miraflores*, three barges, a dredger and a launch from the Pacific level to Miraflores Lake; the time of ascent was one hour, one minute, which delighted the large group of spectators.

The first transit of the Canal was not complete until January 7th, 1914, when the crane boat *Alexander La Valley*, then at Culebra after a trip from the Atlantic, was locked down to the Pacific. Colonel Gaillard did not live to see the completion of Culebra Cut, which had been his special responsibility, for on the day that the Gamboa Dike was exploded he was critically ill with a brain tumour and he died in Baltimore on December 5th, 1913. Goethals wrote of him, "He brought to the service trained ability of the first order, untiring zeal, and unswerving devotion to duty. His name is connected inseparably with the great task which was brought to completion under his guidance, and will be held in lasting honour." Later, President Wilson, by the

Executive Order of April 17th, 1915, decreed that the Culebra Cut should henceforth be known as the Gaillard Cut.

Busy as he still was in building the Canal, Goethals was now beginning to think about its future permanent organization and there was a great deal of discussion about this on all sides. Eventually, after having considered the matter for some weeks, President Wilson signed an Executive Order on January 27th, 1914. It was practically the same as that prepared on the Isthmus and was to be effective as from April 1st. A memorandum was added, stating that the President wished for the permanent operation to come under the Secretary of War, and that certain posts should be made from officers of the Government. For example, an army engineer should be in charge of maintenance, naval officers should be employed as marine superintendents and port captains, naval constructors as superintendents of the mechanical plant, and Public Health Service officers as chief quarantine officers. The President nominated Colonel Goethals as the first Governor of the Panama Canal.

On April 1st he was officially inaugurated as Governor, involving no change of duties, merely a change of title. In addition to being supreme in the Canal Zone, he was also head of the Department of Operation and Maintenance. The design of the locks was based entirely on safety considerations. There were heavy chains across the locks in front of the gates to protect the latter from damage by vessels out of control, guard gates to ensure that vessels would not ram the main gates, and emergency dams to stop the flow of water in the event of failure of the operating gates. There were also interlocking devices on electrical controls, which could be operated only when the operating procedure followed in the required sequence. The unique feature of the Panama Canal is the use of electric towing locomotives, invented by Edward Schildhauer of the Canal engineering staff.

The initial lock operations were conducted in more or less the same manner as suggested by Goethals in 1911. Ships came up to the approach walls, lock personnel came aboard, conducted the vessel through the lock, and then left. This practice was largely based on the barge canal methods used in the Mississippi River, and they proved to be suitable for small vessels and were continued for months. It meant, however, that the work was done by mechanics who lacked experience of handling ships, and the method was strongly criticized by Captain Rodman, who had studied the methods used on the Suez Canal. Goethals referred these protests to a board of three engineers, who did not see the necessity for lock operators to have licences. They asserted that the fundamental principle in the design of the locks was complete stoppage on landing at the approach wall. Handling with locomotives was a matter, according to them, of "applying quickly and positively from a fixed track, heavy power, the power being at all times under complete and perfect control, increased and decreased at pleasure and not subject to modifying influence of wind and current". They conceded that a lock supervisor would not use the same methods of control as a pilot, but they wanted to have "a technical man in charge, specialized in his duties, his machinery, his locks, his currents, his wind".

Before the formal opening of the Canal, Goethals decided to stage a rehearsal transit on August 3rd, using the Panama Railroad ship *Cristobal* for the purpose. For the first transit by an ocean-going vessel he invited a limited number of employees who had been associated with the work for a long time, and amongst them was Philippe Bunau-Varilla, truly a pioneer of this great venture. The *Cristobal* backed clear of the docks and swung into the channel towards the Gatun Locks. Bunau-Varilla was standing on deck, gazing upon the scenes of his former activities with the French Company and talking to a group of people, when a young Canal engineer handed him a copy of the morning paper, which announced Germany's declaration of war on France. Bunau-Varilla was silent, for he knew what it meant. Stepping clear of the group, he crushed the paper in his hand

and, pointing to the entrance to the Canal, exclaimed, "Gentlemen, the two great and consuming ambitions of my life are realized on the same day: the first, to sail through the Panama Canal on the first ocean liner; the second, to see France at war with Germany."

During this transit the lock force, in the role of ship handlers, did not measure up to Goethals' expectations for handling an ocean-going ship. At Gatun the currents caused by the mingling of salt water with fresh sheered the vessel into a dangerous position and one of the towing locomotives burnt out a motor owing to overload. At Pedro Miguel, one of the locomotive towing-cables parted and Colonel Goethals, standing on the lock wall, feared that the *Cristobal* would strike the gates before she could be stopped. The lock at Miraflores was negotiated without any trouble.

However, Goethals was justifiably alarmed, for he at last realized that the lock masters were not ship handlers. The day of the formal opening was approaching, and the operating force was by no means prepared for it. He decided to have lock pilots, who were given an intensive course of instruction in signalling. Captain Rodman issued an order that pilots must board vessels before they reached the approach walls and not leave them until they had cleared the locks. He directed that ships should not be moored to walls, and insisted they should pass through the locks without touching any of the walls.

Dredging had continued on the slide at Cucuracha from the time it had closed the Canal. When the date of the formal opening approached, there was a channel 150 ft. wide and 35 ft. deep, large enough for the Panama Railroad ship *Ancon*, which was to be accorded the honour of doing the inaugural transit from the Atlantic to the Pacific. August 15th, 1914, was the day of the formal opening. When the *Ancon* left Cristobal that morning, the guests included President Porras of Panama and his cabinet, the Diplomatic Corps in Panama headed by Dr. W. J. Price, Minister of the United States in Panama and Dean of the Corps. The guests also included John Barrett, then Director-General of the Pan American Union.

Entering the Gatun Locks at 8 a.m., the *Ancon* cleared the locks into the lake in an hour and a quarter, crossed the lake and arrived at Gamboa at 11.15 a.m. to enter the Culebra Cut. She passed the Cucuracha slide safely and arrived at Pedro Miguel at 12.56 p.m., was locked down to Miraflores Lake and crossed it to Miraflores Locks, where she was locked down again to sea level. She entered the Pacific sea-level channel at 3.20 p.m., proceeded to the channel entrance, and returned to Balboa about 5.10 p.m. Goethals was not on board; he had been watching the operations from the lock walls.

The many thousands of spectators along the line of the Canal witnessed the culmination of this great work as the *Ancon* passed slowly along with its complement of distinguished guests. Perhaps the man who made the greatest contribution to this remarkable achievement was President Roosevelt, for he never ceased to have unbounded faith in its eventual outcome.

7

TECHNICAL PROBLEMS, DEFENCE
AND THE FUTURE

FROM this brief review of a gigantic international under-taking it is clear that the construction of the Panama Canal was the work of many minds and hands.

Pride of place as the pioneer must go to de Lesseps, the genius and builder of the Suez Canal. Although he had the vision and the courage to tackle the Panama Canal, he lacked the means, and moreover suffered severely from complete lack of knowledge of the engineering and financial problems involved. His dislike of engineers was also a grave handicap to his efforts. Adolphe Godin de Lépinay was the man who contributed the most valuable proposal for a high-level canal at the Paris Congress of 1879, but de Lesseps' obstinacy in insisting on a sea-level canal nullified his efforts.

Then there was Henry Abbot, consulting engineer to the New Panama Canal Company, member of the International Board of Consulting Engineers of 1905 for the United States, whose researches on the régime of the Chagres River were indispensable in at last securing the adoption of a high-level canal plan with locks. Philippe Bunau-Varilla, who worked very hard on the Canal as a young man in the days of the Old Panama Canal Company, saw with deep distress the failure of the heroic French effort. He devoted the rest of his life and his considerable influence to a vindication of de Lesseps and the resurrection of the Panama Canal was the chief aim of his life. Indeed, it was claimed that he manœuvred the Panama Revolution of 1903 to the advantage of the United States and was the author of the Hay–Bunau-Varilla Treaty, by which the United States secured the Canal Zone.

Wallace was another outstanding pioneer, for he was the first chief engineer responsible for recruiting the original construction force, breaking the ground and discovering the enormous difficulties and dangers to be expected. Stevens deserves the highest praise for rescuing the Canal from complete disaster, and it was his organizing genius and command of men that prepared the ground so well for Goethals. Goethals was both a great administrator and a highly skilled engineer, and had the power and determination to overcome the inertia that plagues all government procedure and to see the task through to the very end. He was justly famed as the builder of the Canal.

The original plan for the Panama Canal was evolved from many years of engineering study, but it was unfortunate that it had not been based on marine operating experience. The gravest error was the location of the Pedro Miguel Locks at the south end of Culebra Cut and the resulting absence of a summit-level anchorage on the Pacific side of the Canal, an arrangement that caused the severe traffic bottleneck at Pedro Miguel. Miles Duval studied the problem deeply and presented a plan to the Panama Section of the American Society of Civil Engineers in a paper entitled "The Marine Operating Problem of the Panama Canal and the Solution". His plan envisaged the removal of the bottleneck at Pedro Miguel, the construction of all Pacific locks in single structures near Miraflores, and the creation of a large summit-level lake for an anchorage at the Pacific end of the Canal to match the arrangement at Gatun.

He presented the paper on May 20th, 1943, claiming that it was the first comprehensive plan put forward for the improvement of the Canal based on marine operating experience. He believed that with the acceptance of its basic principle of a high-level terminal on the Pacific as the solution for the marine operating problems, it would be possible at last to build the best canal for transiting ships.

It is perfectly clear that for a work of such huge size and vast complexity as the Panama Canal, rapid decisions could not be made by committees with any hope of success. It probably still remains one of the toughest engineering projects ever carried out, demanding skill and endurance of the highest order from all those concerned, particularly from the leaders. The mingling of military with civilian personnel on certain parts of the work provided most valuable experience, which was put to good effect in two world wars, and in trying to solve the exceedingly difficult problems following from them.

An excellent review of what was entailed from the technical aspect was given in a paper by A. G. Menocal, presented to the American Society of Civil Engineers in 1906. He pointed out that the most difficult engineering problem involved in the construction of the Canal was the control of the River Chagres, which was an important factor in the design of either a lock or sea-level canal. The divergence of opinions among engineers called on to decide the type of canal best adapted to meet the physical conditions prevailing on the Isthmus can be traced to the difficulties connected with that river. This applies both to the control of the floods, in all types of canal, and the provisions for an ample water supply for operating it during the dry season, in the case of a canal with locks.

It is evident that a lock canal is the most economical type, both in cost and time of construction, and that the sea-level proposition is born either of sentiment or of a belief that by its adoption the difficulties connected with the river can best be overcome. Menocal also draws attention to the fact that a sea-level canal pertaining to the nature of a strait is not possible at Panama. The tidal fluctuation of 20 ft. at the Pacific terminus, while the Atlantic end is practically tide-less, makes imperative the introduction of a tide lock at Panama by which ships can be locked up or down, into or from the canal, depending on the stage of the sea level at the time of taking or leaving the waterway. That tidal lock will limit the number of vessels passing through the Canal just as much as a series of locks in a lock canal. Some time will be spent in passing each additional lock introduced, and this should not exceed 30 minutes at each lockage, so that the additional time consumed in passing through a canal with six locks would not be more than three hours, an insignificant delay for a ship that has saved thousands of miles by taking a canal route.

Considering the cost and time saved in constructing a lock canal, as compared with one at sea level, as well as the elimination of the uncertainties and engineering difficulties connected with the latter, it seemed to Menocal that the former type should be adopted, provided the Chagres River could be effectively controlled, an ample water supply provided, and difficult engineering problems avoided.

Let us now consider briefly some aspects of the defence problem. When the Spaniards first arrived in the Isthmus, they found there some sixty different tribes of Indians, totalling about 380,000, whilst the most recent census figures (1950) available give the present population as 805,285, mainly mestizos but including about 70,000 Negroes. There were some 42,000 United States citizens in the Canal Zone in 1953.

On several occasions before the new Republic of Panama had been formed, the United States had been obliged, in order to defend its citizens and property, to intervene and maintain public order. It had therefore been written into the 1903 Treaty that the United States would be responsible for the sanitation of the whole Canal Zone and the islands adjacent to it, including the cities of Colon and Panama, and also for maintaining public order if in their opinion the Panamanian authorities became incapable of doing so. It was also agreed that the United States would assume full military responsibility for the defence of the Republic in the event of aggression from any quarter. Within this understanding the United States has always tried to avoid interference with the administrative and political affairs of the Government, and whenever possible has waited for the Republic of Panama to ask for help before intervening.

Panama has no standing army nor armed forces other than its National Police Corps, which comprises one major, ten captains, twenty lieutenants, 75 second lieutenants and 1,130 of other ranks.

The Canal was still under construction during the First World War until 1916, and when the United States joined the Allies, the enemy aircraft and submarines could not reach Panama, so that surface ships were adequate to protect the Zone from possible seaward attack. Since the construction and sanitation of the Canal Zone had become an exclusively military operation, the whole area was placed under United States military protection. During the war, there appears to have been no record of any damage having been done to the Canal, or to the ships passing through it. If sabotage were attempted at any time, it must have been foiled by the Allied Joint Intelligence Services without any kind of publicity.

In September, 1939, on the outbreak of the Second World War in Europe, the President of the United States placed the Canal and all American property in the Canal Zone under military protection. In 1942, after the Japanese attack on Pearl Harbour, the United States Navy took over defence of the Gulf of Panama and on May 18th, 1942, a new agreement was signed between the Republic of Panama and the United States Government, authorizing the latter to establish a number (given by one authority as 134) of air bases in Panama, on condition that all such bases were relinquished one year after the end of the war. Similar agreements were made with all Central American Republics and also with those South American Governments that controlled the various colonies and islands in the Caribbean, Atlantic and Pacific Oceans.

Apart from the air bases maintained within the Canal Zone, fourteen new ones were built outside the zone within the Republic of Panama, and vast zones were also placed under United States military control. Similar air bases were built in strategic positions at all points of the compass, in

Cuba, Bermuda, Jamaica, Guatemala, Martinique, Trinidad, Colombia, Ecuador and the Galapagos Islands in the Pacific, so that within a short time American aircraft were maintaining continuous patrols of all approaches to the Canal Zone in search of enemy ships and submarines. No civil aircraft were permitted to fly over Panama unless the crew was composed of United States citizens who had been given security clearances, and only if the passenger portholes were blacked out so that no passenger would be able to see the Canal or its defences.

Several German pilots who had served in the First World War established a civil airline in Colombia some years before the Second World War, and it was seized by the authorities, together with all enemy assets in Latin America, as each Republic declared war on the Nazis and their allies. Resident aliens were also interned. At the same time, the United States and the United Kingdom reinforced their diplomatic missions in those countries with Navy, Army and Air attachés as well as security officers, all of whom worked closely together with the Governments to which they were accredited, pooling all information obtainable by various resources. Local action to frustrate the activities of enemy agents in any Republic was taken whenever possible, and all information concerning them was centralized in the Security Headquarters in Panama, and from there transmitted to the Headquarters of the British-American Joint Intelligence Services in the United States.

Lewin was appointed Air Attaché to Central America early in 1943. He was not only the first Air Attaché to be appointed to that area, but also the first who could speak fluent Spanish to be appointed in Latin America! At that time the United States had military missions in many of the Spanish-speaking Republics, and Air, Military and Naval attachés were in close collaboration in all United States Embassies and Legations.

Shortly after his arrival in Central America, Wing Commander Lewin was provided with a suitable aircraft by the American military authorities, so that he could operate

single-handed and act as a liaison officer between the United
States General Commanding Caribbean Defences, General
George Brett, and the appropriate General Officers Commanding in Chief of the British Islands in the Caribbean.
General Brett himself piloted Lewin in his own aircraft over
the Canal Zone, pointing out the defences visible from the air
and asking for his comments. He also gave Lewin authority
to fly in any American aircraft over the zone. As a result of
this complete and friendly collaboration there was constant
interchange of vital information between the two officers.

It should be noted that all the Republics adjacent to the
Canal Zone, as well as the nearby Caribbean and Pacific
islands, had been populated over the years by immigrants
from across the Pacific and from many parts of Europe and
Asia, so that the population was very mixed, and it was never
safe to assume that their patriotism was necessarily invested
in the country of their birth, or adoption. Hence one of the
greatest dangers to be surmounted was the aiding of enemy
ships and submarines by residents of these countries near
the coasts, where there were often suitable creeks and bays
that could be used for refuelling and victualling of enemy
submarines.

Lewin was once approached by one of our agents to help
in the location of a radio station that was thought to be in
deep jungle near the Pacific Ocean on the Guatemala–Salva-
dor frontier. Messages that seemed to be going to enemy
agents and submarines, followed by attacks on shipping,
had been interrupted from there, and it was suspected that
refuelling and victualling was being carried out along the
coast. Lewin invited the authorities to lend him an agent
with air experience, and took off with him at dawn from the
airfield nearest to the suspected area. By first going out to
sea, and thus listening to his own radio whilst flying low
over the water and out of sight of anyone on shore, he was
able to pick up signals, climbing and circling as he flew
inland. Meanwhile, the agent in the aircraft was studying
maps and together they succeeded in locating the radio

station, but they could not be sure on which side of the frontier it was situated. In order to avoid the possibility of any ill feeling, a joint force of armed agents from both Republics was landed near the suspected spot that night. In a few hours the enemy radio station had been completely destroyed, and nobody in the vicinity was left alive.

Yet it was often found that suspected help had not been given to the enemy after investigation of the circumstances, and it was this that made the job so frustrating and yet so interesting. On one such occasion of suspected revictualling, Lewin was asked to arbitrate between British and American secret agents, who had disagreed when a British subject was detained in highly suspicious circumstances in what appeared to be a suitable way for the purpose. The evidence collected by the American agents seemed to be sufficient to justify shooting the man on the spot, but the British security officer opposed such drastic action. On making a low-flying reconnaissance of the area, Lewin noticed unmistakable signs of dangerous sandbanks and shallow water around those places where refuelling and revictualling of submarines was alleged to have taken place. He later obtained charts of these waters and convened a meeting of the agents who had disagreed about the case.

It was quite easy for Lewin to convince everyone concerned that no submarine commander would risk his ship in such dangerous surroundings. Moreover, Lewin was able to produce evidence that the money alleged to have been paid to the arrested man was gained from smuggling over a period of several years. There was also some indication that he had been concerned in white slave traffic. In other words, the "submarine" that had been observed "revictualling" was in fact a smuggler's shallow draft launch leaving the coast on a dark night by well-established navigable channels. Harmony and friendly collaboration being once more restored between the joint security forces and agents, it was finally agreed to keep the arrested smuggler in safe custody until after the war and then to hand him over to the appropriate British authorities, with the incriminating evidence, so that further action could be taken.

As far as Wing Commander Lewin is aware, no actual attack was made on the Canal by air, sea or sabotage during the Second World War, and many thousands of tons of allied shipping passed through. Ships were sunk both in the Pacific and Atlantic approaches to the Canal, and so were enemy submarines.

He has considered the project to build a sea-level canal in Panama to the east of the existing Canal, but doubts whether such a canal would be any more politically stable than the existing one. He points out that on April 5th, 1940, an agreement was signed in San José de Costa Rica by representatives of Costa Rica, Nicaragua and the United States, permitting the last-mentioned to build a canal through the territory of the first two. This would be about 260 kilometres long, not counting the portion through the Lake of Nicaragua. It was established, however, that a difference in water level of 21 metres would entail the construction of from seven to seventeen locks, according to the proposed alternative alignments.

He has also noted that surveys have been made in Mexico, where the Isthmus of Tehuantepec is less than 200 kilometres across as the crow flies, and that the topographical features might be overcome by the use of nuclear power as an explosive, a proposal to which we shall refer shortly. It would probably be a sea-level canal. At the time when the last President-Dictator of Nicaragua was assassinated, it was said that more than 70 per cent of the area of the country was owned by the President's family. Lewin thinks that Mexico appears to be the most stable country in Central America today, for which reason he favours the construction of a canal through the isthmus of Tehuantepec, but it is probable that the engineering difficulties would be very considerable.

The longest of the three routes now being studied for a new Panama Canal is the 93-mile Atrato–Truando route through Colombia, which will traverse land that is mainly swamp and almost uninhabited. The proposed Sasardi–Morti route is 110 miles east of the present Canal and is 48 miles long; the maximum depth would be 1,100 ft. The San Blas route will be the shortest of the three, 32 miles, but the location will be only 45 miles east of the present Canal, probably too close for nuclear explosives to be used for excavation.

The present Canal is now more than half a century old and during the past ten years the traffic through it has nearly doubled, and now amounts to about 12,000 ships a year. Experts have stated that chaotic conditions are likely by 1980, or even before. At present, in 1965, the locks are too small to handle hundreds of ships, including several Aircraft Carriers of the United States Navy.

The main reason put forward by protagonists of a new canal is the fear that, if the present one is overloaded, trade between the United States and many Latin-American countries will be injured. About 80 per cent of all ships using the Canal are going to or coming from ports in the United States; many trade with Latin-American countries, such as Chile, Peru and Ecuador, which send 90 per cent of their exports through the Canal.

Grave concern has been expressed about the economic effect of a new canal on the Republic of Panama. A sea-level canal many miles distant from the present Canal Zone, a 50-mile strip across the Isthmus, might cause considerable harm to Panamanian economy. The Panama City-Colon area, which contains 25 per cent of the country's population, might wither away. The present canal employs 14,000 people, of whom 4,000 are Panamanians and the annual payroll exceeds 45,000,000 dollars. Unless Panama can develop other industries, thousands will be unemployed. Only a small fraction of the present labour force would be required for the operation and maintenance of a sea-level canal.

Some officials have suggested that, if a sea-level canal is built, the present one could be converted to a hydroelectric power scheme at relatively small cost. Critics of this proposal point out that Panama has no iron-ore deposits, and lacks any oil, natural gas resources or skilled labour, so that there is no real need for a new source of cheap power.

The original Canal treaty, signed in 1903, gave the United States in perpetuity: "All the rights, power and authority which it would possess and exercise if it were sovereign" in the Canal Zone. The treaty was revised in 1936 and again in 1955, when the United States increased the rate of annual payment to Panama from 430,000 dollars to 1,900,000 dollars. Since 1955 there have been differences between the two countries over the question of more rights for Panama in the Canal Zone, and requests for more financial aid. In the meantime, the United States has sounded the Colombian Government on the possibility of building a canal through Colombian territory.

The House Merchant Marine and Fisheries Committee, which has studied the canal problem, has stated, "The ultimate solution of the basic problem is probably a sea-level canal; but its construction should await a traffic volume that can support the large cost." This Committee did suggest a stop-gap solution in 1960—the building of a third set of locks for the present Canal, at a cost of some 700,000,000 dollars. Since then, however, the prospects of using nuclear explosives for excavation have improved. An official in the Canal Zone, speaking on the proposal to build a sea-level canal with the aid of nuclear explosives, stated, "The use of nuclear energy may not be as spectacular as putting a man on the moon, but it could be equally important for United States prestige throughout the world."

Writing in *The New Republic* of February 1st, 1964, Reinhold Niebuhr pointed out that the crisis between the United States and the Republic of Panama would not be solved by anything Panama agreed was "just". Some Panamanians suggest that only complete acquisition of the Canal will suffice; a partnership will not, in their view, be satisfactory and certainly would not meet the wishes of the United States. An "advisory committee" for the Canal, consisting of members of the Organization of American States, has been suggested, but the instability of Latin-American politics rules this out.

Niebuhr comments that Americans are embarrassed to have the Panama affair remind the world that their country was engaged in overt imperialism in the Spanish-American war. In that war, the American Government had both a Pacific and a Caribbean empire, and the United States needed the Canal for strategic reasons. The Panamanian rebels against Colombia knew what President Theodore Roosevelt wanted, and American gunboats were ready to force the issue. The Canal was built on Panamanian territory, and a perpetual lease was signed. "How ungrateful of Panama not to recognize us as the authors of their independence," writes Niebuhr. "Yet, illegitimate sons are not frequently fond of their fathers."

The economic power, technical skill and strategic needs of the United States were responsible for the building of the Canal, and Colonel Gorgas was the conqueror of the malarial fevers that infested the Canal Zone. Panama by herself could not have done anything about these achievements. Since the Second World War, six Presidents of Panama have been deposed by revolution and one has been assassinated.

In an article by James H. Stratton in the April, 1965, issue of *Foreign Affairs*, reference is made to the hearings before the Joint Congressional Committee on Atomic Energy, when Dr. Glenn Seaborg, chairman of the Atomic Energy Commission, estimated that "at the optimum" it would take five years to develop the devices and nuclear excavation technology for a canal project and that the cost of the programme would be about 250,000,000 dollars. At least part of the cost would be a charge against a sea-level canal excavated with nuclear explosives.

An adverse and possibly critical factor is that radioactive fall-out cannot be discounted and there are still differences of opinion on this vitally important subject. Nations all over the world do not wish to risk the danger of fall-out. A waiver by the signatory nations to the test-ban treaty might be secured if Russia and the other powers have projects on which they intend to use nuclear explosives.

Extensive studies were made during 1946 and 1948 under congressional approval. Thirty sea-level routes from Tehuantepec in Mexico to the Atrato River in Colombia were evaluated, and the conclusion reached was that the best route would be that of the present canal. The estimated cost of conversion was calculated at 2,300,000,000 dollars. Since then improved technology has offset rising prices, so this figure is still valid. A sea-level Canal built by conventional methods in any other country would probably cost twice as much as converting the present Canal.

It has been claimed that excavation and dredging of more than 1,000,000,000 cub. yds. of earth and rock could be undertaken in a way that would not interfere with canal traffic. This would be accomplished by leaving water-retaining natural formations in place to maintain canal levels during excavation. When excavation had been completed, the dikes would be demolished by blasting them into deep pits dug in advance. Lowering of the lock canal water to sea level would take place over a period of seven days which would be the only time in the estimated ten-year construction period when canal traffic would be disrupted.

Mr. John Kelly, director of the U.S. Atomic Energy Commission, in considering the possible peaceful uses of atomic energy, has written: "Our studies show that a sea-level canal could be dug with nuclear explosives for less than one-third the cost and in about half the time conventional methods would require. And a canal excavated by nuclear blasts would be wider and deeper than a conventionally dug canal."

Knowledge gained from Project Sedan in 1962, when a nuclear device of 100 kilotons power formed a crater 320 ft. deep in the Nevada desert, has contributed a great deal to this technology, but more tests in various types of ground are essential. Studies have indicated that the proposed Sasardi–Morti sea-level canal, about 48 miles long, would cost about 800,000,000 dollars if nuclear explosives were used. Otherwise the cost would be 5,100,000,000 dollars (in the U.S.A. a billion is a thousand millions). The respective nuclear and conventional costs for the Atrato–Truando sea-level canal would be 1,200,000,000 dollars and 4,600,000,000 dollars. Conventional cost estimates have been based on a canal 600 ft. wide and 60 ft. deep. Nuclear cost estimates are based on a canal 1,000 ft. wide and 250 ft. deep.

In carrying out such work, it is proposed to use nuclear blasts to dig a series of craters, and about 25 explosions would be involved, the craters being linked together by conventional techniques. An official of the U.S. Atomic Energy Commission has commented thus on the probable dangers involved: "Radioactivity can be held to manageable levels. The Project Sedan explosion proved that. The highest dose of radioactivity it produced was approximately half the amount the Federal Radiation Council defines as permissible. Designs now being studied could lead to nuclear explosives with greatly reduced radioactivity.

"At the depths at which the devices would be detonated, rubble falling back after the explosion, not only would act as a filter to reduce the amount of radioactive debris escaping, but would serve also to suppress the thermal, or fireball, effects and cut down the possibility of air-blast damage."

In preparation for route surveys, authorized by Congress, the United States asks for co-operation of the governments concerned without prejudice on either side. However, the action of the Nicaraguan Congress in the middle of 1964 in repudiating the Bryan-Chamorro Treaty, giving the United States canal rights in that country in perpetuity would, if adopted by other countries, limit, if not preclude, the studies.

The need for a canal invulnerable to attack and with adequate capacity for future needs is now very acute. A single sea-level canal could handle all traffic in the foreseeable future, and it would be needlessly expensive to keep the existing Canal in service if a sea-level one is built elsewhere. Even if this is built on the present site, the economy of

Panama will suffer because of reduction in labour for its operation.

If an accommodation is not possible, the alternative will be for the United States to exercise sovereignty over the Canal Zone as a foreign enclave within Panama. This was the state of affairs after the troubles in January, 1965. A complete impasse between the American and Panamanian governments would not necessarily force the United States to seek a sea-level route elsewhere. The 1903 treaty with Panama does not prevent the United States from converting the present lock Canal to one at sea-level.

On June 22nd, 1965, President Johnson asked Congress to appropriate 7,500,000 dollars for a study of the most suitable site for the construction of a sea-level canal connecting the Atlantic and Pacific Oceans. The White House announced that the Interoceanic Canal Commission, which will make the study, must start work before the statutory deadline of June 30th, 1968. The chairman of the Commission is Mr. Robert Anderson, a former Secretary of the Navy, Deputy Secretary of Defence, and Secretary of the Treasury. He has been serving as a United States representative in discussions with the Government of Panama concerning the Panama Canal.

Other members of the Commission are Milton S. Eisenhower, President of Johns Hopkins University; Kenneth E. Fields, a private industry consultant; Raymond A. Hill, a consulting engineer; and Robert G. Storey, President of the south-western Legal Foundation. This body represents a wide range of interests and should produce a valuable report.

The White House stated that most of the funds will be used "to initiate the collection of basic information on the topography, geology and hydrology of potential canal sites". The studies, based on the data gathered from site surveys, will also consider the feasibility of both nuclear and conventional methods of construction. On April 18th, 1965, when the establishment of the Commission was announced by the White House, the President stated that John H. Irwin, jun., would be named as special representative of the United States for interoceanic canal negotiations with other countries on the project for a sea-level canal as representing the State Department.

It has been claimed that a new canal built with the aid of nuclear explosives will provide a transit time for shipping of only four hours, as compared with the eight hours necessary through the present lock canal.[1] Moreover, it could be managed by less than 1,000 employees, as compared with the present labour force of some 15,000, and it may be possible to cut down the toll charges, which now average 5,000 dollars for every ship.

It is claimed that a sea-level canal will be less vulnerable to sabotage and war damage. In the event of war, the blast damage from a nuclear missile could put the present Canal out of commission for as long as seven years, whereas a direct hit on a sea-level route would knock it out for only a week or two.

The present Canal cost some 380,000,000 dollars to build more than fifty years ago. The minimum estimate for a new canal, using conventional excavating methods, has been given as 2,286,900,000 dollars. By using nuclear explosives, it is claimed, a sea-level canal could be built for 770,000,000 dollars, a figure given in 1960, based on nuclear technology current at that time. A more recent estimate has been given at less than 600,000,000 dollars. When nuclear blasting is employed, earth and rock are ejected and a vast crater is formed. Some debris will inevitably fall back into the crater, but most of it will be thrown clear. It has been proved by testing that the final dimensions of the crater can be controlled by using a device of the right size, located at the appropriate depth.

In 1951, for example, an atom bomb with a yield of 1·2 kilotons (equivalent to the explosive energy of 1,200 tons of T.N.T.) was set off underground. It produced a circular

---

[1] "A New Canal—dug by Atom Bombs", *New York Times Magazine*, September 20th, 1964.

crater 53 ft. deep and 258 ft. in diameter. Later, another shot with the same yield, but placed deeper, produced a deeper and wider crater. With added experience gained from successive tests, more particularly since 1957 when the Atomic Energy Commission's programme was under way, scientists have been able to forecast with growing certainty the probable size of the crater that can reasonably be expected.

In Nevada in July, 1962, the Sedan test shot was carried out with a thermonuclear device giving a yield of 100 kilotons. The charge was located at a depth of 635 ft., forming a crater 320 ft. deep and 1,200 ft. in diameter. This gigantic blast displaced 7·5 million cub. yds. of earth and rock. Tests have proved that if nuclear explosives are placed at the right distance from one another, and if all these charges are exploded at the same time, practically no rocks and earth will be ejected at the ends of the craters. The result should be a smooth and continuous ditch rather than a series of separate craters, which means that a series of nuclear charges can blow away, section by section, enough material to form a channel adequate for navigation without further excavation.

One location proposed for a new canal is the Sasardi–Morti route in Panama, about 110 miles east of the present Canal. It would be about 60 miles long and would cross the Isthmus of Darien between Caledonia Bay and San Miguel Bay. The area is thinly populated jungle, containing only four towns, the largest with a population of less than two thousand. Two towns are just over 25 miles from the site of the nearest proposed nuclear explosion, the third is about 15 miles away, and the fourth is closer to the proposed line of operations.

The plan would entail a year of preliminary work along the route, followed by three years of canal construction. In the first year, geological surveys and some two hundred borings would be made to test the rock formations and measure their extent. Base camps would be established, one on the Pacific and the other on the Atlantic side of the route, served by a system of roads. The camp sites would have living quarters, medical facilities, cold-storage warehouses, offices, shops, dock facilities and loading and storage areas. Between them, these camps would house about 2,700 workers at the peak period of construction in the first year. During actual construction, however, there would be a maximum labour force of about 4,500.

In order to create this canal, it is proposed to set off some 325 nuclear charges. Their average spacing would be about 800 ft., the depth below ground varying from 650 to 2,600 ft. Heavy drilling rigs of standard oilfield type could be used, and when the holes had been drilled, they would be lined with steel casing. It has been estimated that drilling and casing will take about $2\frac{1}{2}$ years on the basis of a 24-hour day and a seven-day week. The plan calls for setting off the explosives in sections—about fifteen charges to a section—working from both ends of the canal, proceeding inland as holes are drilled and lined.

After excavation has moved inland, the dredging of about $10\frac{1}{2}$ miles of approach channel would have to be undertaken in the sea at each end of the canal. By conventional methods, some 15,000,000 cub. yds. will thus be excavated and removed by barge to be dumped in deep water far out at sea.

Proposals for building a new Panama Canal are being actively considered by the United States, and it was announced in April, 1964, that sites in four American nations are under consideration as possible routes for a sea-level canal. A ten-man team of cartographers, engineers and helicopter pilots have mapped a possible route in collaboration with Colombian representatives. Discussions are also being held with Nicaragua, Costa Rica and Panama to set up arrangements for new surveys. When President Johnson announced the agreement with Colombia for the canal survey at a press conference he said that several alternative routes would have to be studied carefully before a final decision could be reached.

Shipping forecasts indicate that interoceanic traffic will exceed the capacity of the existing Panama Canal by 1980.

Since it will take several years to plan and build a new canal, preliminary surveys are now in hand. A sea-level canal is favoured because it would have a greater capacity, provide faster transit time for ships, and be more reliable than a canal that depends upon a system of locks.

The United States Senate approved a canal survey bill in March, 1964, and this was passed to a committee of the House of Representatives. The bill will authorize the President to create a seven-man commission to study the feasibility of a sea-level route across the strip of land connecting North and South America. Traffic along the 51-mile existing Canal doubled during the 1950s, mainly as a result of the increased shipping owned and operated by Latin-American countries. Moreover, very much larger ships are now being designed by the maritime nations, many of which cannot use the locks of the Panama Canal. Ships must be raised 85 ft. by these locks and then lowered again before passing out of the waterway, with the result that present transit time ranges from 12 to 14 hours.

As we have already said, it may be possible to use the power of nuclear explosions for excavating a new sea-level Panama Canal, and the news that three American companies have formed a group to exploit this source of power for such purposes is some indication that it is being seriously considered. This new organization is known as the CER Geonuclear Corporation.

Research on harnessing nuclear power for excavation work was started in the United States in 1957 under the Plowshare programme, run by the Livermore Laboratory, which also develops weapons for the Atomic Energy Commission. A series of tests has been carried out in the Nevada desert to discover how nuclear bombs could be made to excavate craters at minimum cost and with minimum release of radiation. A one-megaton bomb can produce a crater of 1,000 yds. diameter and to a depth of 690 ft. in desert alluvial deposits at a cost of about 3 cents per cub. yd. This figure does not cover development costs and would rise considerably if radioactivity were strictly controlled, as it clearly must be for any practicable engineering project.

Reduction of radioactivity involves placing the bomb deeper in the ground, thereby decreasing the efficiency of the explosion from the civil engineering point of view. Preliminary studies of nearly every project considered, including a proposed new Panama Canal, have shown that nuclear explosives could reduce the cost of conventional blasting methods from a half to a tenth. The engineers in charge of the Plowshare project claim that even with large nuclear bombs, in the megaton range, fall-out debris can be contained within a very few miles of ground zero, and that atmospheric fall-out would be practically negligible.

Ground contamination is quite another matter, for the radiation that remains in the ground can be carried for many miles by underground water. It is clear that very careful geological and geophysical surveys of any proposed construction site will have to be carried out, but these can take so long that the cost of nuclear explosives might be raised to a point where they become uneconomic.

It has been stated by Professor Pauling that all atmospheric radiation causes some generic damage to future generations, though the figures so far obtained are too controversial to summarize briefly, and that there are also many other more familiar and immediate side effects. Until the significance of these is better understood, extreme caution must be exercised, and before any Plowshare project is put into actual operation, those responsible must be quite sure that the money saved will be balanced against the human life that may be endangered.

American officials believe that a final decision on the site for a proposed new canal will be possible towards the end of this decade. On the other hand they believe that ten or fifteen years would be sufficient for negotiating the necessary treaties, making on-site inspections and constructing the new canal, which should then become operational by the early 1980s. This time element reveals that the two treaties, on the present Canal and on a proposed sea-level one, are inter-related; the present Canal may now be regarded as self-liquidating. Present estimates prove quite clearly that by the year 2000 the capacity of the present Canal will be seriously deficient, and a sea-level route will therefore be vitally necessary.

As soon as the sea-level canal is in operation, the present one will revert to the Panama Republic, but its operation will then be too costly to maintain. Thus, should the present Canal not be chosen for the site of the new one, it is expected that certain economic adjustments will have to be made, because of the effects of the cessation of its operation on the economy of Panama City, Colon and indeed the whole Republic of Panama. Some 60 per cent of the present economic benefits for Panama are derived from the Canal; the other 40 per cent are contributable to the operation of the American Army bases in the Canal Zone.

So far as the financing of canal construction is concerned, American experts point out that several options exist, including international financing, but this is one of the questions that will be dependent upon the new canal treaty. From the technical point of view, engineers no longer believe that the 17 ft. difference in level between the Pacific and Atlantic tides will pose a difficult problem for a sea-level route, because the current created will be manageable.

Concerning the proposal to use nuclear explosions for excavation, it has been pointed out that this method will clearly be impossible if the present route is chosen for the new canal, as the density of population would be prohibitive. Apart from this, however, there is the vexed question of the existing test-ban treaty which would have to be discussed with other nations, and some solution would have to be found.

Whatever is decided about the best and most economical way of building a new Panama Canal, there can be no doubt that it will entail an immense amount of rock blasting, excavation and earth moving. In an excellent review of materials handling in opencast coal mining in Great Britain, Caseley gives some idea of what the work on the present Canal actually entailed. He writes, "Over 300 million tons of overburden material were excavated and handled in the opencast mining of coal in the United Kingdom in the one year 1957, for the winning of approximately 14 million tons of coal. This is equivalent to saying that in that one year, the quantity excavated and handled was about equal to the whole of that carried out in the construction of the Panama Canal, which took more than seven years."[1]

A study of this article and other material published about opencast mining methods will reveal much interesting information relevant to the present problem. During the last few years there have been considerable developments in the design and application of very large excavators, and in the use of exceptionally long belt conveyors of high capacity.

One of the most remarkable civil engineering jobs at present being undertaken is the construction of the Portage Mountain dam on the Peace River in British Columbia. The dam, with its impermeable core, will contain 60,000,000 cub. yds. of material, and will have a height of 600 ft., a length along the crown of 6,700 ft. and a maximum width at the base of 2,700 ft. The crown width will be about 40 ft. and the area of water impounded by this huge structure some 680 sq. miles, making it one of the largest inland lakes in the world.

This dam is being built by the Government of British Columbia, and the water in the lake will be used to generate 2,300 MW of hydro-electric power.

The material for the dam is being transported over a distance of 15,000 ft. by the world's longest conveyor, manufactured and installed by Pohlig-Heckel-Bleichert Vereinigte Maschinenfabriken AG, who are represented in Great Britain by Cowlishaw, Walker and Co., Ltd., of Stoke-on-Trent, to whom we are indebted for this information. The material for

[1] "Materials Handling in Opencast Coal Mining", by J. R. Caseley, C.B.E. B.Ss. (Eng.), M.I.Struct.E.—*The Colliery Guardian*, January 10th, 1964.

the Peace River dam consists of glacial moraine gravel, weighing 109 lb. per cub. ft., the grain size ranging from fine sand to pieces with a maximum dimension of 8 in., the proportion of this large size being about 1 per cent. The normal capacity of the conveyor is about 10,800 tons per hour, and the maximum 14,000 tons per hour, the belt travelling at a rate of 1,147 ft. per minute. Power is provided by two electric motors, each of 850 h.p., at the head drive, and by two motors of the same output at the tail drive. Fig. 9 shows this simple

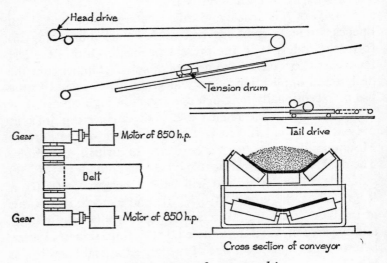

9. *Arrangement of conveyor drive*

drive and the equally simple method used for tensioning the belt; the driving drum has a diameter of 57 in. with a rubber friction lining. The tensioning gear is controlled by means of a pressure measuring gauge.

A Mitcham steel cord belt is employed, and is of special interest because it incorporates two different types of rubber in its construction. The combination of these layers, each having a different tear resistance, produces a laminated effect similar to that of plywood. This means that the fully loaded belt has a high tear resistance which will limit any possible damage that may be caused by heavy, sharp-edged lumps of rock falling on it.

The steel cords of the belt are so strongly bonded to the rubber that if attempts are made to strip the rubber from the steel cords the rubber will break before the bond is destroyed. Any small cuts or gouges that may occur in the covers of a steel cord belt can easily be repaired by the use of hot or cold vulcanizing methods. This type of belt has remarkable flexibility, mainly because there are no plies or cords in the weft direction, and also owing to the all-rubber weft in the steel cord belt. Steel cord belt is today running on some conveyors with idlers troughed at an angle of fifty-five degrees, thereby allowing more load to be carried for a given belt width with certain materials. This high flexibility ensures that the steel cord belt will trough evenly on all types of idlers (the rollers over which the belt runs). In addition, the maximum possible contact is obtained with the idlers, thus ensuring perfect tracking of the belt, whether it is empty or loaded.

Experience has proved that this type of belt is suitable for handling heavy materials, such as iron ore, minerals and overburden. There is no loss of belt strength at the joint. Any belt can be pierced and will rip if the strain imposed upon it is great enough, but the steel cord belt will withstand such unfair treatment better than fabric belting. It may eventually rip along longitudinally between the wires, but such a rip can be quickly repaired. The damage to a fabric belt would be greater, simply because a rip in a fabric belt will proceed longitudinally only so far and then will shoot at right angles across the belt.

Belts of this unique construction have now been running for nearly ten years in installations of exceptionally high power, carrying loads of more than 15,000 tons per hour, and at present more than 400 miles of this belting are at work all over the world. The belt has no fabric in its construction, the steel cords being surrounded by rubber and placed in the warp direction only. These cords are generally

8

situated equidistant from the top and bottom of the belt, and the rubber on and around them is vulcanized into a solid mass.

Another outstanding example of what can be achieved with belt conveyors is provided by the Radar North open-cast coal site in Northumberland, the contractors for which are Derek Crouch Ltd., who are undertaking the work for the National Coal Board. This site contains 7,000,000 tons of some of the best general purpose coals available in that part of the world, and they are in brisk demand for export and for shipment to power stations in the South of England. The site covers an area of about 1,000 acres and the total quantity of excavation is about 134,000,000 cub. yds.; the average depth of excavation is nearly 230 ft.

The plant used for excavation includes a Marion 7800 electric walking dragline with a boom of 240 ft., a dumping height of 118 ft. and a dumping radius of 210 ft. There is also one Bucyrus Erie electric shovel with a 6-cub. yd. bucket, which is employed in conjunction with eight Caterpillar rear dumpers each of 35 tons capacity. The bucket wheel/conveyor installation consists of one Krupp bucket wheel excavator with a wheel of 18 ft. diameter, on the circumference of which there are eight buckets, each with a capacity of about $\frac{1}{2}$ cub. yd., and which has a service weight of some 300 tons.

The electrically driven conveyor installation is about 5,000 ft. long, the width of the conveyor belt is 40 in. and the speed is 510 ft. per minute. This wheel excavator works in conjunction with a Krupp truck-mounted spreader which has a boom length of 93 ft., a service weight of 90 tons and a handling capacity of 450 cub. yds. an hour.

In the method of working adopted, a box cut of some 11,000,000 cub. yds. was first excavated and placed to tip adjacent to the final void. The cut was taken out at the deepest end of the site and was designed to enable all subsequent excavations to be placed below the final restoration level, thereby eliminating double handling. The remainder of the operation was programmed in a series of cuts 100 ft. wide, progressing in order across the site.

One of the main problems encountered has been the removal of the glacial drift material covering the site, the thickness of which varied from 30 to 80 ft. This material could not be cast into the bottom of the previous void by dragline as it would have caused the spoil bank to slip. When more than 40 ft. thick it could not be handled in one lift by the shovel and to split it into two lifts would have meant travelling dumpers along a clay track, which was considered to be an almost impossible task. It was therefore decided to adopt the German system of movable conveyors fed by a bucket wheel excavator. This system has been operating since November, 1961, and has proved to be both economical and practical.

The bucket wheel excavator digs a face of glacial drift up to a maximum height of 40 ft., feeding the excavated material on to a face conveyor, from which the material is elevated to ground level by an elevating bridge conveyor feeding on to a frontal transverse conveyor. This in turn feeds on to the dump conveyor, from which the material is taken by a spreader and placed in position on top of the dragline and shovel spoil banks. All the conveyors can easily be moved to new working positions by a tractor with a side boom attachment, in phase with the progress of the excavation.

The Westfield site in Fifeshire, for which the contractors to the National Coal Board are Richard Costain Ltd., is yet another example of well-planned conveyors. For a distance of some 1¾ miles, millions of tons of rock and shale are being spread over land that is largely derelict, the final total amounting to some 50,000,000 tons. The area is being progressively covered with soil, and it has been estimated that more than 300 acres of new agricultural land will be created. In this case, also, long lengths of belt conveyors have been used in conjunction with swivelling spreaders mounted on crawler tracks.

The largest opencast anthracite site in Great Britain is at

Maesgwyn in South Wales, where George Wimpey and Co., Ltd., are employing a Ransome and Rapier W.1800 type walking dragline, electrically powered, with a bucket capacity of 40 cub. yds., a boom of 247 ft. length, a digging radius of 230 ft. and a dumping height of 100 ft., as the main instrument for handling the vast volume of overburden that has to be moved to uncover the coal seams. The other electric walking dragline is a Marion 7400 machine with a bucket of 13 cub. yds. capacity and a boom of 175 ft. length.

The average depth of the excavations is about 300 ft., the overburden above and between the coal seams consisting mainly of hard shales and about 20 per cent of sandstone. All overburden down to what is known locally as the "eighteen feet" seam is removed by shovels in lifts of from 30 to 40 ft., the rock having been previously blasted to obtain sufficient fragmentation for the efficient excavation of the material. After the above coal seam has been extracted, the W.1800 walking dragline takes over and digs and casts the remaining overburden in cuts 120 ft. wide. Operation of this huge machine continues day and night because the ratio of overburden to recoverable coal on the site is 35 to 1, almost certainly the highest ratio being worked anywhere in the world for coal. By the time the site has been worked out in about 1971, some 6,000,000 tons of coal will have been extracted, which means that about 181,000,000 tons of overburden will have been moved by the walking dragline and other excavators. This site is noteworthy for the excellent maintenance shops where the earth moving equipment is kept in first-class condition.

Caseley has pointed out that several unique features are embodied in the W.1800 walking dragline machine. Previous heavy-duty machines of this type were of all-welded construction because they were generally intended to complete their full working life in one mine. But experience in both Great Britain and the United States has proved that these large electrically driven machines have a very long working life (it can be assumed to be at least thirty years if the machine is well maintained), and with the increasing need to move the machines to new fields, by dismantling and re-assembling them, the designers decided to build up the whole of the structure from individual units. None of the units weighs more than 42 tons, and they are bolted together at the site with Torshear friction grip bolts. Flange welding is used in the site assembly and is kept to a minimum, having been specially designed for easy cutting out when the machine is dismantled. The output of this machine is approximately 40 cub. yds. per hour per cub. yd. of bucket capacity, or 1,600 cub. yds. per hour.

It may be possible to excavate a new Panama Canal with the aid of nuclear explosives, but here the main problems will be political and strategic, and it is very doubtful whether they can be successfully surmounted. We believe that it will be necessary to plan for the excavation and movement of many millions of cub. yds. of material. This will certainly call for the use of explosives on a very large scale, and full advantage should be taken of the fact that today many operators in this type of work manufacture their own explosives at the mine. The explosive is packed into cylindrical polythene bags to fit the diameter of the shotholes as drilled, and often a saving of well over 50 per cent is obtained on the blasting costs, as compared with those of a decade ago. The explosive is made by mixing ammonium nitrate with oil fuel, and apart from economy it has the additional advantage that it is safer to handle than some of the proprietary brands of high explosive that were formerly used. A new form of detonator fuse has also been introduced, which can incorporate millisecond ($\frac{1}{1.000}$ second) delays in the firing of certain holes, and these, suitably distributed, can produce improved fragmentation with less explosive than before.

A paper dealing with the use of ammonium nitrate as an explosive in conjunction with a special type of rock drill was presented to the second Pacific Regional Conference of the International Road Federation in Tokio by Mr. Brian Borthwick, who is the Technical Representative for Atlas

Copco in South-east Asia and is based on Kuala Lumpur.[1]

In South-east Asia, and particularly in Thailand and Malaya, ammonium nitrate has become a very popular explosive. It costs from 20 to 25 cents a pound as against 1.00 to 1.40 dollars a pound for normal high explosive. It is used for a wide range of opencast blasting operations, and to a limited extent for underground work. For most blasting operations this explosive may be assumed to have about the same blasting effect as the normal high explosives used regularly in this area, but it even offers advantages over conventional high explosives because of the high charge density that can be achieved by employing pneumatic loaders. To take full advantage of the cost-saving possibilities of ammonium nitrate, it is essential to have a high capacity, highly flexible drill rig which can provide the necessary blast holes at minimum cost in materials ranging from hard rocks to boulder alluvia and even semi-soft laterites and clays. Such variation of strata would probably be encountered in building a new Panama Canal.

These requirements are claimed to be fulfilled by the new Atlas Copco rock-drill type BBE 51, originally designed and developed jointly between Atlas Copco AB, Stockholm, and the large Swedish contractor Skånska Cementgjutereit. This machine formed the basis for the overburden drilling method first used on a large scale by the above contractor on the construction of the Lindö Canal in Sweden. Mr. Borthwick personally undertook extensive tests with this method in Malaya, in collaboration with Mr. Robert Kenrick, the State Engineer of Pahang. The tests proved conclusively that there is practically no material that cannot be drilled with this rock drill. An even more important discovery was that the method does not require a high standard of skill from the driller or from the shot firer.

From the drilling results obtained with this machine it was

[1] "The Impact of Ammonium Nitrate and of the Atlas Copco Rock-Drill Type BBE 51 on the Economy and Efficiency of Hard Rock Drilling and Blasting of Alluvia and Overburden." Atlas Copco, Ltd.

found that the life of the drill rods, shank adaptors and couplings was extended by more than 50 per cent compared with the life of the same rods used in the Atlas Copco rifle bar rock drill of the Bison type, which has the same piston diameter. It was also found that, whereas this rig requires a comparatively large volume of compressed air, its high drilling speeds and freedom from stoppages caused by stuck drill bits gave substantial savings in consumption of compressed air per foot of drilling.

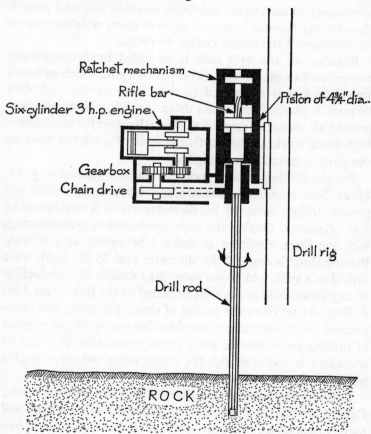

10. *General arrangement of the Atlas Copco BBE 51 rock drill for drilling overburden*

It will be seen from Fig. 10 that this machine is both simple and robust. The percussive action is provided by a powerful piston of 4¾ in. diameter moving up and down in a cylinder. As a refinement to the machine, the piston is rotated in the cylinder by a normal rifle-bar mechanism which serves to ensure an even distribution of lubricant within the cylinder and uniform wear on both piston and cylinder. However, as this rotation mechanism is only required to turn the piston in the cylinder, these parts may be considered as having an indefinite working life, and even if they should become worn no serious harm would come to the machine if the piston ceased to rotate.

Rotation of the drill rods is provided by a six-cylinder compressed air motor with an output of 3 h.p., which operates smoothly and is connected to the chuck of the rock drill through a gearbox and chain drive. As it is a standard compressed air motor designed and normally used for continuous high-speed work, in this particular kind of work the wear on the parts is practically negligible.

For the drilling of hard rock the machine can take 1¼, 1½, 1¾ or 2-in. standard extension rod equipment, which will permit drilling from 1¾ in. diameter up to a maximum of 5 in. diameter. During the tests conducted in collaboration with the State Engineer at Bukit Ubi quarry at Kuantan, Pahang, four holes of 3 in. diameter and 75 ft. depth were drilled in a shift, which was more than double the production of any other drilling rig used or tested at the quarry on 3-in. drilling. Apart from the saving of time, drill rods, and compressed air, there is also a considerable saving in the number of drilling crews needed for a given production. A range of sprockets is available for the chain drive, which will give higher or lower maximum speeds.

For very large-scale operations in building a new Panama Canal, the selection of the best method of working will mainly depend on the local geology. In recent years German engineers have made remarkable advances in the design and construction of belt conveyor systems for transporting materials over unlimited distances in their dry state, and depositing and spreading them to final grades and levels in spoil banks that may be below or above the point of discharge of the conveyor system. All this can be achieved with a single integrated set of plant capable of working round the clock and independent of weather conditions. In a well-planned system of this kind there can be a great saving of manpower and running costs.

It should be emphasized at this point that there is nothing new about the use of conveyor belts for the transport of materials, but in the past no really satisfactory method had been devised for feeding the excavated materials into the system or for delivering them into deep spoil banks or over extensive areas of land. Nor was it possible to secure adequate mechanical synchronization of the operations involved.

Some problems still remain to be solved, such as the feeding of hard rock into the system without excessive "intermittency", but the advances that have been made are summarized by Caseley as follows:

(a) The securing of greater flexibility of movement at the points of junction of the separate conveyor sections as well as at the feed and delivery ends, so that they can all be moved progressively with the advancing faces without any interference with continuity of throughput.

(b) The slewing of the belts laterally by a single mechanical contrivance mounted on a crawler tractor which requires one operator.

(c) The movement of the belt longitudinally where required by mounting the sections on rail tracks.

(d) Provision to discharge material at the delivery end, over a sufficiently large radius and at varying levels, above or below the belt level so that any further handling of material is practically negligible.

(e) New designs of belting which incorporate steel cable longitudinal reinforcement enabling these belts to carry heavier rock loads up steep gradients and at higher speeds than were previously possible. The Mitcham belt, already

8*

described above, is an outstanding example of this, as proved by the Peace River job in British Columbia.

At the Radar North opencast mine in Northumberland, described above, the bucket wheel excavator, with conveyors and spreaders, works ahead of the large walking dragline and feeds the drift material on to the conveyor system, which in turn, by means of the spreader, places it in its final position behind the workings on the top of the longitudinal spoil banks cast by the dragline. The bucket wheel excavator works a 5½-day week of eleven 12-hour shifts with half an hour in each shift for maintenance. The dragline works a 6-day week of twelve 12-hour shifts using three operators, each working an 8-hour shift.

On the above basis, the wheel excavator and conveyor system handles about 54,000 cub. yds. of drift material during a working week, and the walking dragline 120,000 cub. yds., giving an average of about 174,000 cub. yds. of overburden dealt with each week, all of which is deposited in its final resting place.

At the Westfield opencast mine, already briefly described, the conveyor system is just over two miles in length, and its purpose is to transfer a total of about 25,000,000 cub. yds. of overburden material from the mine area to low-lying land in an adjacent valley. The material mainly consists of hard to very hard shale and sandstone, which cannot be excavated and fed on to a conveyor system by a bucket wheel excavator. It is excavated by four 5-cub. yd. capacity electric face shovels, from which it is transported by side-tipping dumpers, each of 20 cub. yds. capacity, into large ground hoppers located within the mine, and which in turn pass the material through large crusher feeders on to the conveying system. The first section of this conveyor brings the material up from the mine at a gradient of 1 in 8 and at a speed of 800 ft. per minute. It then travels by way of two more sections to the fourth and final slewing section, where it is deposited into the final position by a spreader machine.

The omission of the bucket wheel type of excavator,

directly connected and feeding at the input end, and its substitution by the face shovels served by dumpers, does sacrifice to some extent the advantage of "non-intermittency" in this method. However, that is largely overcome by the provision of adequate capacity in the ground loading hoppers at the crusher feeders, of which there are four, and provided that at least three are kept loaded at any one time, there is little likelihood of the "non-intermittency" of the conveyor equipment being broken. The use of side-tipping dumpers at this point also helps to maintain continuity at the feeds since no reversing or backing-up of the vehicles is required when discharging into the hoppers, as is necessary when discharging from rear-end tipping dumpers on embankments.

Before mining could begin on the Westfield site it was necessary to divert a public road and several services and watercourses. The southern part of the site was covered by a peat bog, and since the peat was thixotropic (thixotropy is the property of finely divided solids in suspension setting to a gel if left undisturbed) it had to be removed before excavation of the underlying material could begin. It was decided that dredging would be the most efficient method of removal, pumping the material into lagoons. The walls of the lagoons were constructed from drift material obtained from the northern part of the site, having a maximum height of 65 ft. and containing about 3,750,000 cub. yds. of material. The dredger, of the cutter-suction type with a head of 7 ft. 6 in. diameter mounted on an arm 71 ft. long, was brought to the site by road, in sections, and built in a dry dock on the site. The dock was then flooded and the dredger cut its way into the area to be dredged. About 4,300,000 cub. yds. of peat, sand, silt and clay were removed by the dredger at an average rate of 9,000 cub. yds. of material in the solid per week.[1]

The coaling area is small in comparison with the maximum depth of 400 ft., so that it was not possible to work the site

[1] Paper by W. G. Martin, M.C., A.M.I.C.E., presented to the Symposium on Opencast Mining, Quarrying and Alluvial Mining, London, Nov., 1964.

by normal strip mining methods. The first phase of the mining development was therefore an open-pit mine, which served as a box-cut for the disposal of the overburden from the second phase of the mine development. The overburden and coal partings (26,000,000 cub. yds.) had to be disposed of clear of the excavation area. A suitable disposal area—a valley containing a bog and surrounded by poor agricultural land—was available about a mile south of the site.

Alternative methods of transport for the overburden from the mine to the tip were considered. The route to the tip area crossed a stream, a railway and two roads, and in order to transport the material to the tip in dumpers it would have been necessary to build bridges at these points so that haulage could continue without interruption in all weathers. The Opencast Executive decided that the most satisfactory method of moving the material was by crushing and conveying. At the time of letting the contract for the first phase of the mine, the Executive had installed the conveying plant and part of the crushing plant.

The rock drilling equipment consisted of two Joy 58 BH Champions, one Reich 675, one Reich 600, and one CPTG 800; these were all track mounted drills with the exception of the lorry mounted Reich 600 machine. The four larger machines were fitted with drills having roller bits; the two Joy drills and the Reich 675 machine were used for the preparation of overburden for blasting, drilling holes to a depth of 85 ft. in order to blast a face 80 ft. high.

In the initial stages of the work at Westfield, ammonium nitrate and oil fuel were mixed together as the explosive. Water in the boreholes caused trouble and it was found that polythene bags did not keep the explosive dry. After unsuccessful tests with cardboard tubes and rigid polythene containers, it appeared that sealing the explosive in 16-gallon tin-cans was likely to be the most successful solution to the problem. There was still some difficulty, however, because the cans tended to float in wet blast holes and the blasting was not uniformly satisfactory.

Experiments were then carried out in collaboration with the manufacturers of explosives, using explosives based on T.N.T. and nitroglycerine, which are very powerful and are also unaffected by water. However, such explosives cost twice as much as the ammonium nitrate–fuel oil type, but they do permit the use of larger holes spacing, with the result that drilling costs are reduced.

Difficulty was found at first in initiating the explosion of the high explosive, but the solution was to employ a primer with a very high velocity of detonation. Present practice is to use 5 per cent by weight of primer in each shothole, as compared with 10 per cent by weight when using the ammonium nitrate–fuel oil explosive. A factory was set up on the site for the manufacture of the nitroglycerine type of explosive. Regulations governing the manufacture of this type of explosive in Great Britain are very stringent, and it is only on a long-term contract that the cost of setting up a suitable factory can be incurred.

Four Ruston Bucyrus 150 type excavators were provided for the excavation of the overburden, working across the pit from west to east, removing the overburden in benches 80 ft. high. The rock is loaded into side and rear dumpers of 18 cub. yds. capacity for transport to the crushers. In view of the need to produce rock that can be handled by the crushers, primary blasting is much heavier than that required merely for efficient excavation by machines of this size, but in any case the drivers have to ensure that no rock is too large for loading to the crushers. In the early days of this site, as an experiment, steel bars were fixed across the mouth of the excavator bucket to ensure that no oversize stones would be loaded, but the output of the excavators was reduced to such an extent that the idea was abandoned. In its place a course of instruction was introduced, including a spell of working as members of the crusher crew for the excavator drivers, who were then well aware of the delays and loss of output that were incurred when oversize rock was loaded.

The crushed rock is fed on to a steel-cord belt 48 in. wide, travelling at a speed of 800 ft. per minute and having a rated capacity of 3,440 tons per hour. The belt has three fixed sections and one slewing section, the overall length being 11,000 ft. The steel cord has high tensile strength and a low stretch factor, so that it is suitable for use in long single flights; it is also highly resistant to possible damage by impact.

The slewing belt referred to above operates on the surface of the tip, the tail of the slewing belt receiving the material from the head of the last fixed belt and conveying it to the spreader unit. When first installed, the slewing belt was extended in line with the last fixed belt. As the material was tipped on the left-hand side of the slewing belt, the belt was gradually slewed in an anti-clockwise direction on the tipped material until it was at right angles to the last fixed belt. The slewing movement having been completed, the slewing belt will now move along the fixed belt and at right angles to it, taking the material off the fixed belt by means of a tripper.

The spreader is mounted on crawler tracks, and has a jib 92 ft. long which can be rotated through an angle of three hundred degrees. A high-speed conveyor belt mounted on the jib receives the material from the connecting bridge and throws it out to form the tip. The driver, sitting in a cabin alongside the jib, can control the movement of the spreader, its connecting bridge, and associated tripper, along the length of the slewing conveyor, forming the tip in predetermined contours as he moves. The slewing conveyor is moved by means of a D7 tractor with a special roller attachment, which is first fixed to the flat-bottomed rail on one side of the conveyor. The tractor then moves the length of the conveyor at a slight angle to it, dragging the conveyor towards a new position, a few feet at each pass.

Before reaching a definite decision on the most suitable location for a new canal, we should glance back over the past history of the two great works of Ferdinand de Lesseps, one an outstanding success, the other a tragic failure. In the case of the Suez Canal, this great diplomat thought that by making the ruler of Egypt the largest individual shareholder, as well as the major dividend beneficiary in the operation of the Canal, and by insisting that the shipping of all nations should have equal rights of passage, he had done everything possible to ensure its adequate defence and economical operation, in peace and war. Yet the Canal was annexed from the French by force of arms in "peacetime"—and no Israeli shipping or merchandise has been allowed to pass through since the annexation.

Similarly, de Lesseps made the Colombian Government a shareholder in his Panamanian concessions, and the United States Government, having bought the French concessions as well as having fomented and financed the Panama revolution, also bought from the Panama Republic a defence zone five miles wide on each side of the Canal route. The rental for this strip of land has been increased at least twice since the original purchase contract was ratified, yet the political relations between the United States and Panama have gradually worsened throughout the years since the Canal has brought relative progress to what was once a neglected area of swampland belonging to Colombia.

These grim facts serve to emphasize that neither diplomacy nor statesmanship can keep pace with world political evolution, yet it is equally true that, so far as is known, neither of the two Canals suffered materially during both world wars, simply because the controlling powers took adequate and immediate steps to defend them from sea and air attack and sabotage. With the development of atomic bombs and nuclear-powered submarines, however, no canal or area anywhere in the world can be considered safe from aggression and destruction in the event of war.

Apart from political problems that may hamper the future operation of the Panama Canal, it is clear that the Canal is inadequate for the rapidly increasing tonnage of ocean-going shipping. A second and preferably sea-level canal is desirable somewhere across the Isthmus, located as far as possible from the existing one. Since global defence needs develop more rapidly than the political stability of Central America, it seems that the most suitable location will depend upon the longest smooth operation that can reasonably be expected in "peacetime".

Of all Spanish-speaking countries today, only one has been fortunate enough to avoid internal political bloodshed this century, and that country is not in Central America, so that the choice must be governed by the relative political progress in this area, where Costa Rica and Mexico appear to be the most advanced. Even so, the renting of a piece of territory "in perpetuity" today would not appear to be very successful.

Engineering techniques have advanced to such an extent since the time of de Lesseps that the choice of a new route depends more on finding a progressive democratic form of government in a country that shows definite signs of political stability. An agreement that will be mutually acceptable to both contracting governments will then have to be made.

On September 24th, 1965, President Johnson announced that the United States had agreed to abrogate the 1903 Panama Canal Treaty. A new treaty will give Panama sovereignty over the Canal Zone and a share in operating the Canal. This decision should facilitate negotiations for the building of a new sea-level canal across Central America. It is probable that the new canal will be across the Isthmus of Panama, but no decision has yet been made.

President Johnson said that the treaty would provide for an American share in defence of the Canal under "base rights and status of forces agreements". This is the type of agreement under which American troops are stationed in Europe and elsewhere. Referring to long outstanding Panamanian complaints of discrimination, he said, "Both countries recognize the important responsibility they have to be fair and helpful to the employees of all nationalities." He said the new treaty would last for a certain number of years, or until

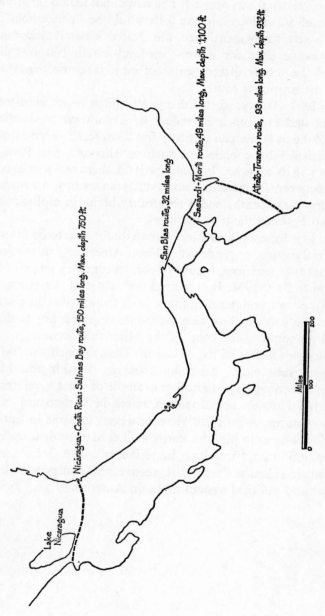

11. *Four alternative routes for a new Canal*

Lake Nicaragua

Nicaragua–Costa Rica: Salinas Bay route, 150 miles long; Max. depth 750 ft.

San Blas route, 32 miles long

Sasardi–Morti route, 48 miles long, Max. depth 1,100 ft.

Atrato–Truando route, 93 miles long, Max. depth 932 ft.

Miles

0   100   200

the sea-level canal was opened. The new canal would be open to ships of all nations and the tolls would be "reasonable". As we have already mentioned, the United States is studying four possible sites for a new sea-level canal, but it will probably be ten or fifteen years before it is in use. Fig. 11 shows the proposed routes.

The 1903 Treaty, dictated by Washington soon after Panama had become independent of Colombia, treats the Canal Zone as American territory but local feelings have not been satisfied by concessions such as allowing one Panamanian flag to be flown. In January, 1964, there was a pitched battle between Panamanian and American troops, resulting in twenty-three deaths and a temporary break in diplomatic relations between the two countries.

President Johnson's decision will no doubt help to counterbalance the anger engendered in Latin America by a resolution that the American House of Representatives passed on September 20th, 1965. It expressed the "sense of the House" that American unilateral military intervention was justified if there was a "threat" of Communists taking over any Latin-American country—an echo of the Monroe Doctrine.

Although officials of the American State Department have expressed misgivings, generally speaking Washington has ignored the move as just another example of what is referred to as the House's occasional exercises in flamboyant but empty gestures. A different view, however, prevails in Latin America. For example, the Peruvian Legislature denounced the resolution as "American Imperialism". The Colombian Legislature called it "openly regressive and contrary to the judicial and political system of Latin America".

SELECTED BIBLIOGRAPHY

American Society of Civil Engineers, *Transactions*, New York, December, 1927, pp. 946–67.

BEMIS, SAMUEL F. *The American Secretaries of State and their Diplomacy*. New York: A. A. Knopf, 1928. Ten volumes.

BENNETT, IRA E. *History of the Panama Canal; its Construction and Builders*. Washington, D.C.: Historical Publishing Company, 1915.

BERDEAU, R. W., Jun. American Society of Civil Engineers— Paper No. 1412, *Transactions of the American Society of Civil Engineers*, Vol. 82, 1918.

BIDWELL, CHARLES T. *The Isthmus of Panama*. London: Chapman and Hall, 1865.

BIGELOW, JOHN. *The Panama Canal and the Daughters of Danaus*. New York: Baker and Taylor Company, 1908.

BISHOP, FARNHAM. *Panama, Past and Present* (Revised Edition). New York: Century Company, 1916.

BRESSOLLES, PAUL. *Liquidation de la Compagnie de Panama; Commentaire ... de la Loi du premier juillet 1893*. Paris: A. Rousseau, 1894.

BUNAU-VARILLA, PHILIPPE. *From Panama to Verdun; My Fight for France*. Philadelphia: Dorrance and Company, 1940.

BUNAU-VARILLA, PHILIPPE. *The Great Adventure of Panama*. Garden City, New York: Doubleday, Page and Company, 1920.

BUNAU-VARILLA, PHILIPPE. *How to build the Panama Canal*. Lecture before the National Geographic Society in Washington on November 29th, 1905.

DE LESSEPS, FERDINAND. Discussion on Interoceanic Canals, with his answers to questions by J. Dirks, published in the *Transactions of the American Society of Civil Engineers*, Volume 9, March, 1880.

DE LESSEPS, FERDINAND. *Recollections of Forty Years*. Translated by C. B. Pitman. New York: D. Appleton and Company, 1888.

DUVAL, CAPT. MILES, U.S.N. *And the Mountains Will Move*. Stanford University Press, 1947.

ENOCK, R. *The Panama Canal*, Collins, London and Glasgow, 1914.

GOETHALS, GEORGE W. *The Panama Canal: an Engineering Treatise.*

GORGAS, WILLIAM C. *Health Conditions on the Isthmus.* Engineering Record, Vol. XLIX, May 14th, 1904.

INTEROCEANIC CANAL CONGRESS, Paris, May, 1879.

KIRKPATRICK, RALPH Z. *Reference Book on the Panama Canal*, July 20th, 1939.

LIDGERWOOD MANUFACTURING COMPANY, Elizabeth, N.J. *Rapid Unloaders for Discharging Dirt, Ballast, Rock or Ore.* 1919.

LINDSAY, C. T. *A Short History of the Panama Railroad.* Address before the Caribbean. Chapter No. 21, National Sojourners. Colón, June 17th, 1936.

MENOCAL, A. G. *The Panama Canal.* Paper No. 1021. *Transactions of the American Society of Civil Engineers*, Vol. 56, 1906.

NATIONAL ACADEMY OF SCIENCES, WASHINGTON, D.C. *Preliminary Report upon the Possibility of Controlling the Land Slides Adjacent to the Panama Canal.* April 15th, 1916.

OTIS, FESSENDEN N. Isthmus of Panama. *History of the Panama Railroad and of the Pacific Mail Steamship Company.* New York: Harper, 1867.

PANAMA CANAL, THE. *The Panama Canal, 25th Anniversary, August 15th, 1939.* The Panama Canal Press, 1939.

RICHARDSON, ALBERT D. *Personal History of Ulysses S. Grant.* Hartford, Connecticut: American Publishing Company, 1885.

ROOSEVELT, THEODORE. *Theodore Roosevelt; an Autobiography.* New York: Macmillan and Company, 1914.

SCHONFIELD, HUGH J. *Ferdinand de Lesseps.* London: Herbert Joseph, Ltd., 1937.

SHELDON, R. C. *A History of the Construction, Operation, and Maintenance of the Panama Railroad.* 1933 (Thesis presented to the Ohio Northern University).

STEVENS, JOHN F. *An Engineer's Recollections.* New York: McGraw Hill Publishing Company, 1936.

WYSE, LUCIEN N. *Le Canal de Panama, L'Isthme américain, explorations . . . un plan panoramique du Canal de Panama supposé achevé, un tableau synoptique des divers projets.* Paris: Hachette and Company, 1886.

INDEX